GABRIEL

ALBERT M

POOLBEG

A Paperback Original
First published 1991 by
Poolbeg Press Ltd.
Knocksedan House,
Swords, Co. Dublin, Ireland.

ISBN 1 85371 081 4

Poolbeg Press receives financial assistance from the
Arts Council/An Chomhairle Ealaíon, Ireland.

Cover design by Peter Knuttel
Typeset by Typeform Ltd.
Printed by The Guernsey Press Ltd.,
Vale, Guernsey, Channel Islands.

Chapter 1

Gabriel Gabbett lived in Dalkey, seven or eight miles south of Dublin, with his two older brothers and baby sister. His father, Harry, worked in a bank in Dublin, and his mother, May, worked much harder looking after them all.

They did nothing extraordinary for most of the year, but they spent some of the summer at the seaside in County Wicklow. They travelled there in a hired car. It was black, all straight in shape with wooden slats running along the roof which was surrounded by a small metal railing to keep the luggage from falling off. The boundary between Co Dublin and Co Wicklow is just north of Bray. It is marked by a roadsign and as they crossed the children cried out, "We're in Wicklow—*now*!" and they felt that the holiday had really begun.

The house they rented was at the end of a lane leading down to the sea. It was white with a slate roof, and in the grass around it you could find four-leaf clover, not far from a wild fuchsia bush.

The visit to Wicklow was the high point of the year, but Mrs Gabbett did not enjoy it very much.

For her it meant cooking on a two-burner paraffin-oil stove with few utensils. She had, however, the help of a maid who was encouraged to believe that she too, was enjoying a holiday.

The boys spent their days on the strand or leaning over the parapet of the little stone bridge crossing Potter's River at Brittas Bay. It was one of their pleasures to try to spot trout lurking in the shadows a few feet below, so that they could pelt them with stones, bits of stick, and any other missiles they could find.

There was a small cottage near the bridge. Its porch had been converted to serve as a sweet shop, and they spent their pennies there. The best value was a bag of broken biscuits or a length of liquorice telegraph wire. Sherbet, in a small round wooden box equipped with a flat metal spoon, was good value too, but not on a windy day.

The road branched at the bridge, and one branch curved to climb a small hill and give entry to an old house covered in a pink wash. They had spent earlier holidays there, but Mrs Gabbett said it was haunted, and never slept a wink any night she was in it. She said she had the feeling of being watched by someone standing near her bed. She had related this experience to one of the old local women, known as Mrs Mac, who was a marvel to see. She was very tall and thin, and dressed in black from head to foot. She even had a black handkerchief which she kept in the pocket of her cardigan. She was thought by the boys to have a perpetual cold, because whenever she spoke her words were broken by sneezes and applications of the black handkerchief to her streaming nose and eyes. This continual discomfort turned out to be self-inflicted, for the handkerchief was impregnated with snuff which she kept in a little tin box in the pocket of her cardigan. From time to time she dipped a corner of the handkerchief in the snuff and applied it to her nose, each side in turn. Within seconds she would sneeze and turn her head from side to side until she finally settled in her chair and gazed into the fire with bleary eyes.

When Mrs Gabbett confided her fears about the pink house to Mrs Mac, she got a knowing look in return, and silence. When pressed for an opinion, the old woman told her of a man without a head who was seen to sit on the parapet of the bridge at Brittas on certain nights of the year, but no one knew who he was. "How could anyone?" the children reasoned, for if he had no head, no one could recognise him, and anyway, if he were headless, he was also eyeless, and could not look at anyone at all.

At harvest time the fields of wheat, barley or oats were cut by a reaper and binder drawn by a pair of horses. They plodded around each side of the crop until that remaining was reduced to a small square. Then the machine was hauled away to allow someone to walk through to frighten out rabbits. Whenever one did break out it was chased and despatched with a blow from a stick. Very few escaped, and as many as fifty or sixty would be killed in an afternoon. Few if any were eaten; they were thrown into ditches.

At the end of the summer, the next exciting event was the threshing, done by a travelling contractor whose machine was drawn and powered by a steam engine which would arrive in clouds of steam and smoke.

When the children heard the chuffing and clanking of the approaching monster they ran to meet it and trotted along beside it feeling its heat and smelling the hot grease and the coal. The driver was a kind and tolerant man, for he stopped to allow one of the children to climb on to the tiny footplate as he shouted, "Keep well back from dat fire, or yeh'll be destroyed." Then he would lift up his passenger to the whistle chain and shout, "Pull dat." When the child did so, there was a pathetic wet gurgling squeak from the brass whistle on the boiler. "Not too long, mind, or yeh'll use up all de steam, and we'll be here all night."

Eventually, amid shouts and shudders the engine, with its great flywheel spinning and its wide iron wheels scrunching to dust the surface stones of the road, would arrive at the field where the great rectangular rick of corn stood. Getting the whole contraption through the narrow entrance required orders and instructions and running about of happy helpers until the untidy lot was safely positioned, and everything made ready for the work to start.

The next morning men on top of the threshing machine cut the twine binding each sheaf as it was thrown up on the end of a pitchfork. The corn was fed in and the grains separated to be spewed out into sacks at one end while the straw was pushed out at the other by moving flat paddles.

When the rick was reduced to the last layer, the threshing stopped to enable everyone to help in pushing stakes into the ground in a circle around the whole area of operations. Sheets of board and corrugated iron were leant against these to provide a flimsy, low perimeter wall. This prevented rats which had made their home in the base escaping, and as the last sheaves were removed, they began to run out.

Now, chasing rabbits is one thing; they are comparatively docile and easy to deal with, but rats are different. They have a reputation for viciousness, and attack when menaced. The children had heard stories of a man's being bitten by one, suffering blood-poisoning and dying. So they stayed outside the low wall, and hoped that rats could not jump too high. The work was left to two or three terriers, which to cries of "Rats, Rats," chased around killing as fast as they could.

At the end of one summer holiday two boys the Gabbetts knew well were killed by a motor car. They were riding down the lane towards the sea on the same bicycle when they collided on a curve with a car coming up the hill. Gabriel watched them being placed in the car to be taken to the hospital in Wicklow. They were limp, and covered in blood and dust. He knew they were either dead or dying. Within a few days the children were little affected by the event, but the dead had been their friends, part of them, chasing rabbits and running on the strand in the sun.

**

The Gabbetts' house had three bedrooms. The family slept in two of them, while the maid had the third. The maids were girls from the country who were boarded and given a uniform, or two in fact: a blue overall and large white apron with matching cap for morning wear, and a black dress with tiny apron and white cap for afternoon wear. They were paid £24 a year, and had an afternoon off once a week. One of their duties was to take the children walking in the afternoons if the weather was fine enough. Sometimes they went along The Metals, a pathway atop the railway cutting, to Glenageary station to watch the trains, and came home by a different route, kicking the leaves of the chestnut trees along the Silchester Road.

They walked all over Dalkey, and up and down the surrounding hills, but the favourite walk was to Victoria Park in Killiney, to climb to the top of the hill which dominated the surrounding countryside. They looked to the south across Killiney Bay to Bray Head and the Wicklow Mountains, to the north to look over Dublin Bay, and eastwards to the sea. They checked that the black hull of the Kish Lightship was still there, and at the right time of the day looked out for the mail-boat from Holyhead. Three ships maintained the service: *Cambria*, *Hibernia* and *Scotia*. They each had adopted one of these as his own; Cambria was Gabriel's, not because he knew or cared for Wales, but because he liked the sound of the word. "Cambria, Sambria, Bambria, Tambria," he often sang out to himself. You could not do this with Hibernia or Scotia, at least not with the same euphonious result.

On the summit of the hill there is a square building surmounted by what looks like an inverted ice-cream cone which can be seen for miles. A little further down the hill there is a solid square structure made of stone blocks on top of which there is another similar but smaller square set back on the four sides by a few feet, and then a third layer on top of this, and so on in pyramid fashion until the smallest square at the top. The boys never knew who had made these useless buildings, nor why, but the pyramidal square served as a wishing place. You had to walk around each level seven times going up and down without losing count. This was very difficult to do, so they were never surprised that wishes seldom came true.

*   *   *

An aeroplane crashed into the sea off Dalkey Island, and when the wreckage had been located, Mr Gabbett took the boys to Coliemore Harbour to watch the salvage operation. The harbour is very small, and is used only by lobstermen, and to shelter the rowing-boats hired to people who want to visit the island. The Gabbetts pushed themselves through the crowd, to stand at the end of the pier.

Not far out to sea, and heading towards the harbour-mouth were some small boats tied to each other in line ahead. Among those in the leading boat was the Gabbetts' greengrocer and ice-cream man. Seeing him gave Gabriel a sense of identity with the event, and made him feel important. The men in the last boat were leaning over the side holding ropes attached to something in the water, and as they drew nearer it was possible to see one of the aeroplane's wheels. Gradually it was manoeuvred into the harbour, and extra ropes tied on to pull it closer to the steps let into the pier. All hands pulled, and as the wreck was lifted, the body of the pilot still strapped in the cockpit was revealed. He was wearing a brown leather helmet similar to the one Mr Gabbett wore on his motorcycle. Gabriel stared at the man closely. He did not look at all like the boys at Brittas Bay. He was as white as paper, and showed no sign of injury. The crowd was silent, and apart from the lapping of the water there was nothing to hear. Mr Gabbett put one of his hands over Gabriel's face to cover his eyes, but he was still able to see everything through his father's fingers. This was not very comfortable, but he reasoned that if he pulled away the hand, he might have been taken home and see nothing more. He wondered why his father had taken him there in the first place if he did not want him to see anything.

When they returned home and Mrs Gabbett heard about the dead man, she told Mr Gabbett she did not think it was right to have taken the boys to see him. He just snorted, "Nonsense woman. What difference does it make?"

This was a typical reaction because, though he was a kindly man, Mr Gabbett thrived on disasters, and was happy to share any he came across with anyone. He was attracted to tragedy; he did not gloat over or take pleasure in one, but he felt he had to visit the scene of any event of a dramatic nature, especially if someone had been killed. He even had expressions of concern for those involved. He was a great man for the human interest story. If he heard of the death of a fireman, for example, he would go to the house or factory where the event had occurred, and if there was a policeman or anyone else there wearing an official-looking cap, he would say something like, "Terrible business, terrible. People should be more careful."

If a policeman were shot, an event not unknown in the Dublin of the 1930s, he would go to see the place, and when he came home would relate his impressions of the incident and give retrospective advice on how the victim could have saved himself. If a car drove into the Liffey he would go to the point of entry and watch the water flowing past for ages, and then tell the children later they should always beware of water, and never to go near the edge of the quay.

Apart from golf, Mr Gabbett's sporting interest lay in shooting birds. Everything from snipe to geese flew in mortal danger in his vicinity. He was a great shot, he never had to fire twice at the same target, and often brought down two birds with a quick right and left. He trained his own dogs. He was quite expert at this, and had the infinite patience and application required to be successful. Gabriel's favourite dog was a black and white cocker spaniel. She was a very good gun–dog, and highly thought of by Mr Gabbett until she disgraced herself by eating a dead duck he had left with her while he and Gabriel had been absent for only a few minutes. The offence was all the worse because Mr Gabbett had assured Gabriel that the duck would be all right. "A good gun–dog never

11

eats the game," he had said, but when they returned the dog greeted them with wagging tail and a mouth festooned with feathers. Nearby were a few remains: more feathers, two little legs with webbed feet, and fragments of meat and bone. "Well curse that bloody dog," Mr Gabbett said, picking out the most colourful feathers to fashion a cockade for his hat.

When he was not shooting birds, Mr Gabbett went ferreting for rabbits. He did not have his own ferrets but borrowed a pair from the local handyman, Mr Webb. With the ferrets in a box they went on the motorcycle, two of the boys and the ferrets in the sidecar with the other boy on the pillion seat. They drove until they saw a likely place in a country field, and walked along the hedgerows to find burrows which they sealed off with nets, just leaving one open for the rabbits to escape into range of Mr Gabbett's shotgun. There might be a long wait, and Gabriel sometimes spent his time picking bunches of cowslips and buttercups which he took home to place in a tumbler of water on his bedside table. If there were no rabbits, the ferrets kept coming out of the burrows and tried to get back into their box, but on occasions they were very successful, and the Gabbetts went home with two or three rabbits. Following one of their better days, Mr Gabbett decided to breed his own ferrets. "We would have a constant supply of rabbits," he told Mrs Gabbett, "without being under any obligation to Mr Webb." He bought a buck and a doe, and within a short time they produced a litter. The children took over the newcomers as pets as soon as they were weaned and let them climb up inside their jackets to go to sleep in their armpits. The ferrets became so tame that they were never taken rabbiting in case one of them should be lost. They were pampered and overfed, and Mrs Gabbett had to buy rabbits from the butcher to feed them.

Not put off by the failure of the ferret scheme, Mr Gabbett next acquired a greyhound, not a pup, but a full-grown animal, capable its breeder said, of outstripping Mick the Miller on a good day.

The dog's official name was Rathdown Lad, but he was called Boris. Gabriel made himself responsible for feeding and grooming him, and took him for walks every day. They became great friends.

Mr Gabbett hoped to race Boris in Shelbourne Park, and at weekends he and Gabriel went in the fields off Barnhill Road to train him. While Mr Gabbett held the dog's collar Gabriel ran ahead a few hundred yards, and then with a wave of his handkerchief he signalled to let Boris go, whereupon he galloped at full speed to Gabriel's beckoning arms.

There turned out to be difficulties which prevented the dog's entry to Shelbourne Park, but nothing daunted, after several months' training Mr Gabbett and the boys, with Boris stuffed into the bottom of the sidecar went to a flapper meeting being held in a field near Stepaside.

There was a large crowd and about a dozen bookies present. The course was straight and marked out by white tapes strung along sticks driven into the ground. There were six dogs in each race, and when Boris's turn came, Mr

Gabbett stood at the finishing line while one of the older boys was detailed off to "slip" the dog at the starting signal. Gabriel positioned himself at the side of the track about three-quarters of the way down the course. Boris got off to a good start and was leading the field.

"Come on Boris. Come on Boris," Gabriel shouted at the top of his voice.

Now Boris knew Gabriel far better than he did Mr Gabbett, and on hearing his master's cries, obediently left the race and bounded to him, wagging his tail with joy.

"I'm finished with that bloody dog," growled Mr Gabbett later, as angry as he ever got. "Thank God I didn't bet on him."

On his Wicklow holidays Gabriel had met Jerry the postman who taught him how to take salmon from Potter's River. Visitors normally fished with rod and line for brown trout. For those in the know, however, salmon were there for the taking, and Gabriel was quick to learn how. The most skilful way was to lie prone on the river bank parallel to the flow of water, facing upstream. An arm was put gently into the water and slowly moved about to feel if a fish were lying against the bank. If one was found, it had to be "tickled": it was stroked gently with the fingers as the hand was moved closer to the head, and as the gills were reached a sudden grab with a jerking action landed the fish on the bank.

Another method entailed standing chest high in the river, holding in the upstream hand a cylindrical net suspended from a circular wooden frame which was pushed against the bank low down in the water while a stick in the other hand was moved about to drive any fish into the net.

At night a net could be set across the width of the river and left until the morning, but there was always the chance the fish might be stolen or eaten by otters or rats.

***

Gabriel was sent to Miss Manley's school in Sandycove Avenue. His brothers had already been there for a year or two. His first day set his attitude to school for the future. Miss Manley was in a black-and-white dress covered by an old blue cardigan. She had a necklace of heavy glass beads which made her rattle as she walked. She was bandy, and her lower lip fell away from her teeth to reveal her gums. Gabriel took an instant dislike to her. Her manner was gruff and forbidding when she addressed a few words to him as she conducted him to a room at the back of the house. In it he found ten or twelve other children standing around a dining table reciting their morning prayers. They finished as he arrived and Miss Manley introduced him to the teacher, Miss O'Dwyer. She was very tall with flaming red hair, and walked like a man. Later, Gabriel imitated her walk on his way home, and enjoyed the laughter of the other children.

On the second day Gabriel was in time for the prayers, most of which he knew by heart, but there were a few he had not heard before, and Miss O'Dwyer, noticing he was saying nothing, leaned towards him and said: "Say your prayers."

Gabriel said nothing.

"Say your prayers, I told you," she ordered again, hitting him on the top of the head with a heavy blue pencil. Gabriel remained silent. He did not know the particular prayer, but he could not tell her, because he thought he ought to have known it, and to admit ignorance might bring further abuse. Miss O'Dwyer left him alone, and soon the lesson started.

Within a few minutes one of the children put up his hand, Miss O'Dwyer nodded at him, and he left the room. After a while he returned to his place. Then another boy did the same thing, and this continued until the period ended and they were let out to the back garden to play. Gabriel had not guessed what they had been doing, but a boy called Raymond explained they had been going to the lavatory.

"Where is it?" asked Gabriel.

In answer, Raymond led him back to the house to the foot of the stairs, where he showed him a loop of thick black curtain cord draped around the knob at the end of the bannister rail.

"If that cord is there," he said, "it means the lavatory upstairs is vacant, and if I want to go up I must take it with me and put it around the knob at the top. When I am finished, I must bring the cord down again, and put it back here. That's a Golden Rule, because no one can go up if the cord is not at the bottom."

The next morning, as soon as the children were seated around the table, and before Miss O'Dwyer had arrived, Gabriel left the room, collected the black cord, went upstairs and locked himself in the lavatory. He stayed there until he calculated that the prayers had finished, then returned to the class room and sat down. Miss O'Dwyer ignored him, and he felt quite pleased with himself. The next day he did the same thing with equal success, but on the following morning, as he was sitting on the lavatory seat, he heard footsteps approaching, and almost at once there was a vigorous rattling of the door handle, and he heard Miss O'Dwyer ordering: "Come out here, come out at once."

Gabriel came out and faced her on the landing.

"Get downstairs," she snapped, cuffing him around the ears with her fingers.

Gabriel ran back to the classroom and sat down, saying to himself that Miss O'Dwyer had broken a Golden Rule. If she breaks Golden Rules, so will I, he told himself. Nevertheless, he could no longer escape the prayers, so from then on he gabbled with moving lips, reasoning that if priests could do it in Latin and get away with it, so could he, in English.

After the lesson Gabriel told Raymond about how Miss O'Dwyer had broken the Golden Rule. Raymond was very sympathetic, and so they became friends, but Gabriel was never happy as long as he was in the school. He never got coloured pencils to play with, nor did they ever sing, but there was one incident from which he learned a most lasting lesson which he never forgot. Miss Manley had very strict views on how young girls should dress. Ruth, who sat next to Gabriel at the table, was considered on one occasion to be wearing a dress too short. Miss

Manley made her stand on a chair in front of all the other children while she pinned strips of paper to the hem of the dress until its length was at the correct level below the knees.

Ruth stood trembling with her eyes full of tears, but not crying. What were her feelings? Embarrassment, fear, bewilderment, humiliation, anger even, perhaps all. She still had her baby teeth; she was too young to define her feelings, but what Gabriel felt was compassion, though he too could not have expressed this at the time.

This incident, trivial in execution, supplied the foundation stone on which Gabriel's behaviour towards others was established. A person has rights which are inalienable, and even if no one tells you what these are, they are self-defining in the light of experience.

***

In the summer the boys spent most of their time playing in the fields or paddling in the water at Sandycove Rocks. At low tide there, the sea is separated from the shoreline by masses of rocks and boulders with hundreds of pools of all sizes inhabited by a variety of sea creatures. They caught crabs on hooks baited with pieces of limpet they hammered off the rocks with stones. They put their catch in buckets and carried them home, but sometimes if they had several crabs, they let them scuttle back to the water to see whose would get there first.

When they were not fishing, they worked their way along the shore to the bathing place, the

Forty-Foot. The men who bathed there (no women were allowed) all seemed very old to the boys. Many of them walked about naked, though nude bathing was supposed to cease from early in the morning. Gabriel thought this practice very immodest. He learned this word from his mother who used it to convey that she considered something to be impure, indecent or obscene. Immodest or not, the boys spent a fair time gazing at these naked men, and drawing each other's attention to the peculiarities of some of the organs on display. They kept a look-out for someone they considered sufficiently worthy of comment, and when they did had to cover their mouths to hide their laughter. There was always the fear that one of the men would be annoyed enough to chase them, but they never really feared being caught because they knew they could run away before anyone could get his trousers or a towel on to chase them.

During one hasty retreat Gabriel slipped on seaweed and fell on his nose, which bled so much he had to run home with a handkerchief held to it. Mrs Gabbett made him lie down on the sofa in the front room, and applied cold compresses to his nose, forehead and the back of his neck. She had many home cures: a blocked nose at night-time required the application of petroleum jelly all over the malfunctioning organ and the surrounding area of the face. The boys had great faith in this treatment for it always seemed to work. The fact that the nose would probably have been clear by the morning with or without it never occurred to anyone. When she cut the boys' hair, she rubbed whiskey into the back of their necks to prevent their catching cold, and this practice seemed to be very efficacious too; no one ever had a cold after a haircut. She was a great believer in the power of eucalyptus to prevent or even cure most infections. In particular, she claimed that the presence of the eucalyptus tree in the back garden was responsible for the good health they all enjoyed, and consequently when any of the children sneezed or coughed she produced a bottle of oil of eucalyptus and put a few drops on a handkerchief for the patient to sniff. Her rate of success was prodigious, on the grounds that if a cold did not follow on the day after a sneeze or a bout of coughing, the timely use of the eucalyptus had been responsible.

As for Mr Gabbett, he placed his faith in syrup of figs. If anyone complained of being queasy, he produced a bottle of this vile, brown liquid, and despite protests, administered at least two teaspoonsful which had the result of producing a mild bout of diarrhoea the next day. On his return from work he would ask how many times the patient had been to the lavatory, and on being given a number would say, "There you are then, you needed a good clean-out."

He had a special cure for warts which he claimed was fool-proof: obtain a hair from a horse's tail, make a loop, and place this around the blemish for seven minutes. The wart would soon disappear. On the strength of this information Gabriel decided to obtain a supply of horse hairs for future use. He climbed in between the wheels of Billy the Milkman's float, grabbed a fistful of strands of the horse's tail and pulled. This startled the horse which took off so quickly that Gabriel barely had time to avoid the wheels. Billy chased after the horse, shouting, "Stop, yeh black-arsed bastard."

The boys were delighted with this expression, but were forbidden to use it by Mr Gabbett on pain of having their grandfather told of their disobedience. The old man was Mr Gabbett's father. He was over eighty years old, and lived in Rathmines. The boys were in awe of him and always on their best behaviour in his presence: he could usually be depended upon for at least sixpence on the few occasions they visited him in the year.

The children's other grandparents were dead, but Mrs Gabbett had a maiden aunt who lived in Sandycove and who, for practical purposes, served in the role of grandmother. She was a small plump person who bore a remarkable resemblance to Queen Victoria. She dressed in black ankle-length gowns, plain or with white and purple trimmings. When seated, with her legs on a footstool she looked like a decorated catafalque. She was a religious fanatic, went to at least two masses a day at Glasthule church, and three on Sundays. She attended various public acts of devotion like the rosary and benediction as often as she could, and a monthly sodality meeting. Once a year she went on retreat at Glasthule, and also at St Michael's at the top of the Royal Marine Road in Dun Laoghaire. She never said "Dun Laoghaire" though, always "Kingstown," the name bestowed on the place to commemorate the visit of King George IV.

The children went to see her regularly, and though they were very fond of her, they found her constant sermonizing and advice on spiritual matters very tedious. They always left her in possession of religious magazines like *The Messenger of the Sacred Heart* or *St Anthony's Annals*, and frequently with aluminium medals to protect them from danger physical and spiritual. She gave them scapulars, little squares of brown material decorated with pictures and mystical signs and letters, which were stitched to tapes to be hung around the neck or tied around the waist. Their function was to increase the power of the medals, and she considered them to be the most efficacious of all the sacramentals.

***

Mr Gabbett was promoted manager of one of his bank's Dublin suburban branches. It had living quarters attached, so the family had to move from Dalkey. The move was achieved with the aid of a few men and one of Millar and Beatty's pantechnicons. The kitchenware, crockery and small pieces were wrapped in newspaper and placed in tea-chests. The beds were dismantled and carried to the van with all the other furniture, and when it was time to go the children ran cut to the garden to see if anything had been forgotten; then they returned to inspect each room in the house. These, now all empty, made their voices echo as they shouted with excitement. Mrs Gabbett was in the hall to usher them out and to close the door for the last time. They went down the short path to the gate and out to the pavement to walk the short distance to the tram stop.

They were leaving their fields and friends, their walks and wishing place, the rocks, and all the people and things which had been their world for as long as they could remember: Billy the milkman, the lobstermen and the harbour, the eucalyptus tree with its swing, the gooseberry and fuchsia bushes. When they climbed into the tram jabbering away, they did not know it, but this was the day their childhood ended.

Chapter 2

On moving to Dublin the boys were enrolled at the Catholic University School in Leeson Street, an establishment run by the Marist Fathers. It was about a mile from the new house, and Gabriel went there on his bicycle. There were no lessons on Saturdays, but the school assembled in the hall for choir practice under the tuition of Mrs Boylan. She had glasses dangling from a chain attached to a small circular brooch pinned to the lapel of her jacket. The chain was spring-loaded, and when she took off the glasses, it wound itself into the brooch. For Gabriel, watching the chain going in and out was the most interesting event of the session.

The singing consisted of practising parts of the Latin High Mass: "Kyrie Eleison," "Gloria in Excelsis" and "Credo." The "Credo" was the most boring of all. It was the longest, and Gabriel always gave a very boisterous treatment to the protracted "Amen" at the end, an expression of relief if not of devotion.

Mrs Boylan took it for granted that everyone could read music for she never explained what the marks on the lines in the hymn-book meant. The new boys learned what to sing by picking up the airs from the older boys and in a month or so Gabriel was as good, or as bad, as the rest of them.

Most of the masters were priests but about a third were laymen. Priest or layman, all, with a few exceptions were heartily disliked by Gabriel. He did not like school and did not hide the fact. Consequently the school, as personified by the masters, did not like him. He was not a good pupil: he was not only weak in two or three subjects but in all of them. He had no favourite, he just disliked one more than another, and the degree of dislike was proportionate to his depth of detestation for the teacher in each case, changing with the teachers as he moved up the school.

The headmaster, known as The Beak because of his long curved nose, introduced a system of weekly marks for each subject in a range of two to five; a four or five was satisfactory, but three or less was not, but a three in one subject was cancelled out by a five in another. An excess of threes over fives, or even a single two was followed by a beating. As achieving sufficient fives to cancel threes was beyond Gabriel's capability, he gave up trying, and came to regard his weekly beating as inevitable. There was only one other boy as bad. He was called "Quack" because he walked like a duck and always had a drip on the end of his nose. On Wednesdays, the day the marks were read out in front of the class, the two boys followed The Beak into the school yard to the tuck shop. There, each one was made to stand with outstretched hand, palm upwards,

25

while The Beak, holding the wrist and using his full strength brought down his other hand, holding a foot-long leather strap half an inch thick. He gave at least six blows to each hand. He never spoke to the boys, and when he was finished they had to open the door by turning the handle with both hands, their fingers too numb to function. Gabriel never showed any reaction, he clenched his teeth as he struggled with the door, he made no expression of resentment, no tears came, that might have pleased The Beak. Once outside he went to the washroom and struggled with both hands to allow cold water to flow over his flaming purple-red fingers. He wondered if hot water would have felt better, but there was never any. He resisted the demanding urge to cry in case anyone came in and saw him, but when he could bear it no longer he retreated to one of the lavatory cubicles, and with each hand firmly held in an armpit he cried in silence swaying back and forth on the edge of the lavatory seat. He did not cry in self-pity or in remorse for his scholarly failings, but in seething anger for the sense of injustice he felt at not being taught anything he wanted to know. It would have been more natural if he had reacted to the brutality of his treatment, but this did not occur to him.

The beating went on for years but at no time was there ever any discussion between Gabriel and his teachers. No effort was ever made to find out what was wrong. No talks ever took place with his parents and they remained ignorant of the treatment he was receiving. Gabriel could never tell them, for if he did they might have had it stopped, that would have been a surrender; he would stand up to these pious hypocrites on his own.

The teaching of religion took up more time than any other subject, and before any period in any subject, the teacher led the class in gabbling through three "Hail Marys" in fifteen seconds flat. Every Wednesday morning the school was marched to the chapel for mass, and once a year there was a week's retreat when the boys spent all day hearing sermons delivered by a priest specially imported from one of the order's other houses. No talking was allowed as an act of self-denial. This rule produced its ritual of signs and grimaces which were on the whole more entertaining than being allowed to speak.

The sermons dealt with obedience to the pope and other church leaders and the sureness of eternal damnation for those unlucky enough to be caught by death in a state of mortal sin. Everything was very neat, a boy knew where he stood and, if he did not, any priest would be only too pleased to put him back on the right path. There were sermons on pride and humility, the importance of observing all the religious duties and associated rituals, on the terrible fate awaiting non-catholics who failed to correct their mistakes and repent in time, on the enormity of the offences of Martin Luther (who was mad anyway) and on the serious effects on the soul a visit to a Protestant church had, to say nothing of those to be suffered by any one who took part in, or even attended, a service in one. They were warned of the sins of the flesh, but what these were was never explained (for years Gabriel thought that the worst of these was to eat meat on Fridays) and, because one priest had spoken about immodesty in association with the theme, he came to understand that he was talking about going around in your skin. As this was something he had never seen anyone do (except the men at the Forty-Foot) he felt the matter had no relevance to himself. He thought later, after reflection that the priest was referring to dressing and undressing in such a way that at no time should one be completely uncovered. This posed a serious problem when it came to bathing but as having to account to his mother for wearing his shirt in the bath seemed to him to be less desirable than committing a sin, really against his will, he felt in the clear.

It was at times like this that the definition of rules was so useful. They were told that all sins had to be confessed even venial or minor ones but to leave out one of these, though undesirable, was not sinful. Mortal sins were different. They had to be confessed come what may—to hold one back deliberately was a mortal sin in itself. Mortal sins came in different sizes according to circumstances. It would be a mortal sin to steal sixpence from a beggar but it would be all right to go up to five pounds before the offence became mortal if the victim were a rich man. For a transgression to constitute a mortal sin that would stand up in court, so to speak, three conditions had to be fulfilled: serious matter, (subject to definition according to circumstances), full consent, (you either wanted to do it or you did not), though circumstances could play a large part here too and full knowledge that what was being done was wrong—a debatable point.

The boys were never left in any doubt that all sins of impurity, whatever that was, were definitely serious matter, and so far as these were concerned only the questions of consent and knowledge had to be considered. Consent was relatively easy but the knowledge part caused trouble. Gabriel did not know what this impurity business was, apart from a vague relationship it might have to walking around in his skin. He discussed these points with his friends, but no satisfactory explanation was forthcoming. One boy did supply a clue when he told Gabriel that his father had told him impurity was "when you held your tool except when you actually wanted to pee through it." This did not sound too unreasonable in light of the immodesty business but it was a bit too far-fetched to be believable. Another boy told him that his father had taken him to the cinema, and that during the course of the film a man seated in front of them had "blown-off" very loudly. The boy's father had asked, "What was that?" Whereupon the guilty party turned to them and said in a loud voice, "Don't you know a fart when you hear one?" This upset the boy's father so much, he got up and left the cinema. Outside he told the boy, "Stop laughing. To laugh at that sort of thing is a mortal sin."

Apart from the emphasis placed on sin and its punishment, the boys also learned the six precepts of the Church and the ten commandments of God, of the seven deadly sins and the seven gifts of the

Holy Ghost, of the nine first Fridays, and how to conduct a triduum and a novena; in fact of every aspect of the importance of numbers in religious practice.

It was impressed upon them how important it was to contribute to the cost of the clergy ("the support of our pastors") because the scriptures clearly stated that those who preach the gospel must live by the gospel. Gabriel asked if this could not also mean that those who preach the gospel should live more in keeping with its rules, rather than make a living from it. He was told that the bishops and priests knew better than any one else what the scriptures meant and that his question was the result of misinterpretation and only showed the folly of any lay-person's putting himself forward to question these matters. The constant propaganda had the desired effect: the boys never doubted anything; they attended the weekly school mass willingly (it was better than being in the classroom) and outside school hours some boys, including Gabriel, took part in various religious activities such as going to mass every day during Lent, or trudging around seven Dublin churches and chapels on Holy Thursday.

Gabriel normally went to the Sacred Heart church in Donnybrook, which from time to time was also attended by Eamon de Valera who might hear mass on his way to Government Buildings from his home in Blackrock. He normally timed his arrival to coincide with the beginning of the mass, and took his place at the back of the church. He invariably dressed in black, and in the winter wore an overcoat which all but reached his ankles.

It made Gabriel feel he was in touch to sit beside him and he often hung about outside until he saw de Valera enter whereupon he followed to his pew. He told Mr Gabbett he sat beside de Valera at mass. "I wouldn't do that if I were you," warned his father, "What'll you do if someone takes a shot at him?"

From then on, if ever de Valera sat anywhere near Gabriel, he immediately got up and put what he considered a safe distance between himself and the potential target, well out of the line-of-fire.

Maud Gonne MacBride went to mass on Sundays at the Sacred Heart too. She also dressed from head to foot in black and wore a black veil. "She's in mourning for Ireland," Mrs Gabbett said, and as Gabriel grew older, he knew this to be true.

The only charitable work of any practical value undertaken by the boys at school was the visitation to some poor household to hand over food vouchers supplied by the St Vincent de Paul Society. The boys raised money by annual flag-day collections and donating anything they could themselves. The visits showed Gabriel a side of life new to his experience: semi-starving adults, hungry children, families who spent days in resigned silence trying to keep warm, staring into a fire too small, sheltering in a room not fit for pigs.

Being closer to Dublin allowed for other regular social events to be added to the Wicklow holiday: the Dog Show on St Patrick's Day and the Spring and Horse Shows in May and August respectively. The children were not particularly interested in dogs or horses, but any outing was welcome.

On St Patrick's Day Mr Gabbett took them all to the showground at Ballsbridge. Once inside they split up to go their separate ways, arranging to meet at the exit in time to go home for dinner. Before leaving they each had an indelible mark stamped on the back of the wrist by one of the gate-keepers to enable them to get in again on their return.

There were stalls set up by manufacturers and suppliers of all kinds of goods appertaining to the keeping of dogs, including one where samples of dog biscuits were dispensed in little miniature sacks. The children found these very attractive and lined up several times to get as many bags as possible before being noticed by the man in charge. Gabriel thought the biscuits rather tasty, and ate more of them himself than he gave to dogs lying in their cubicles. As for the dog show proper, he enjoyed watching the obedience tests, particularly if he could safely propel a biscuit in the vicinity of a dog whose devotion to its master was less than its taste for biscuits and was diverted from its duty to the intense annoyance and frustration of the handler and Gabriel's own quiet satisfaction.

Mr Gabbett was not interested in the Spring or Horse Shows, and the children went to these on their own. The main hall of the Royal Dublin Society's premises at Ballsbridge housed the majority of the stalls operated by various commercial interests, and many of these gave away free samples of their goods and copious quantities of glossy pamphlets. To enable them to carry all the loot obtained the children first went to the Nugget Shoe Polish stand which extolled the merits of its product in rhyme:

Whether the weather be wet,
Or whether the weather be fine,
Whatever the weather, the best for the leather
Is Nugget, the perfect shine.

They offered pencils and large carrier bags which were then used to hold all the papers, badges and samples available. Extra badges were got whenever possible to be used as "swaps" at school. The RDS library was used to accommodate workers in arts and crafts, and potters and weavers, basket makers and sweater knitters toiled away all day under the gaze of countless bystanders. In the open, agricultural machinery was on view. There were cattle and sheep, and of course horses to be inspected, and finally, laden with useless paper and full of ice-cream (always described by its sellers as "Cream Ices"), the children walked home to be scolded by Mrs Gabbett for bringing piles of rubbish into the house.

***

The family doctor was a pompous old bore. The children did not see him like that though, they were impressed by him. He wore a black jacket with striped trousers, a gray waistcoat and spats to match. In winter he had an overcoat with an astrakhan collar, topped by a bowler hat. He spoke with an air of profundity, and tended to say everything twice.

33

On the few occasions when Mrs Gabbett's remedies failed he was sent for. He came to see Gabriel who was complaining of stomach ache with a fever. Mr Gabbett, who played bridge with the doctor at his golf club entered the room while Gabriel was being examined. He was carrying a tray with a bottle of whiskey, two glasses and a jug of water. He half-filled both glasses, added a little water, and gave a glass to the doctor, "Ah you're a terrible man Harry," said he, "a terrible man, good luck to you, good luck," and he all but drained the glass in a gulp.

When he put down the tumbler, he said to Gabriel, "I hope you haven't your father's bad habits."

"Arra, a ball a'malt never harmed anyone," interjected Mr Gabbett before Gabriel could say anything.

"All in moderation Harry, all in moderation," said the doctor finishing off the drink.

"Don't bite the top off that," he ordered Gabriel, as he shoved a thermometer into his mouth.

He then proceeded to prod Gabriel's abdomen looking for tender spots, after which he listened to his chest. He took out the thermometer, looked at it, but said nothing. Then, "What are the bowels like boy? What are they like?"

Gabriel knew what this meant. Nothing was found amiss, this was the stock question in the circumstances, and he reported that he considered himself to be all right but the doctor paid no attention, "More movements Harry, that's what he needs, more movements," and without a further word to Gabriel, left the room.

Mrs Gabbett gave him some liquid paraffin, because he flatly refused the proffered syrup of figs. The pain never returned, and a new remedy thus entered the Gabbett pharmacopoeia.

Like many youths, Gabriel developed spots on his face. These caused neither pain nor discomfort, but they were unsightly, and made him feel very self-conscious. They had appeared shortly after he had started to shave and he concluded that he must be suffering from barber's rash. He had seen pictures of this condition in a magazine and, being completely ignorant of its cause, assumed that if he did not stop shaving he would suffer the frightful fate of the wretched man in the picture. Mr Gabbett was the first to notice he had stopped shaving, "Why don't you have a shave?" he asked, "It's no wonder you're all covered in spots."

"I never had any till I started," retorted Gabriel.

"Well a good wash wouldn't do you any harm, and a good clean-out too, if you ask me."

"I don't see why that should have anything to do with it, and anyway I *do* wash."

"You'd better let the doctor have a look at you. I'll tell him you'll be around, when I see him at the club tonight."

When Gabriel eventually visited the doctor in his surgery, he found him seated at a roll-top desk, "Hello, Gabriel," said the doctor, "what can I do for you?"

"It's these spots and pimples," Gabriel answered, pointing to his face.

"Let's take a look, laddie, let's take a look."

He stood up and walked towards the window,

indicating that Gabriel stand close to him, facing the light.

"That's acne, or, to give it its full name, *acne vulgaris.* It'll get better by itself."

"Well, can you give me something to hurry it up?"

"Oh yes. There's a great deal I can do for you, but tell me now, tell me. Have you any, mmmm dirty habits?"

Gabriel did not know what the man meant. To him "dirty habits" meant not washing, so he replied, "No, I haven't."

"You know what I mean, lad?" the doctor asked, with his head on one side, "you know what I mean?"

Gabriel, very puzzled, said nothing. The doctor went on, "You haven't, mmmm touched yourself down there?" staring hard at Gabriel's crotch, and then in booming tones, "Do you abuse yourself, boy, do you abuse yourself?"

Gabriel had no idea what he was talking about. Of course he touched himself down there, he thought, I have to pee, don't I? As for abusing himself, how could he do that? He could abuse somebody else by being rude to him, but how in heaven's name could he abuse himself? He concluded that the doctor was every bit as odd as he always thought he was. He had never thought much of him before and thought even less of him now. Suddenly, it came to Gabriel that the doctor might be talking about something he might have done with a girl, because he had a suspicion that they and young men did things "down there," but he had no idea what they were. He had seen some

36

advertisements in English magazines giving advice on how to recognise venereal diseases, and he was now horror-struck at the thought that this man, this buffoon, had got it into his head that he, Gabriel, had one of these, and that the spots and pimples were all part of some such affliction but this could not be, because he had done nothing. This just made things worse, for he had heard that some of these diseases could be passed from generation to generation, and he was now faced with the shattering realisation that he must have inherited the condition from one of his parents, or even from both of them. How could he find out? What could he do about it? The idea came to him that he should say that he had "done things" with a girl and face the consequences, at least he would be getting the right treatment, but how could he trust the doctor not to tell his father? The shame of the whole thing would be insufferable.

He got no further with these thoughts as the doctor turned from him and sat down again. He wrote Gabriel a prescription for some ointment and told him to wash his face thoroughly at least three times a day. "It'll soon go away, lad, it'll soon be gone."

He led Gabriel to the front door, shook him by the hand and said, "Goodbye, and tell your father to behave himself."

Was there a sinister meaning in this seemingly innocuous pleasantry? Gabriel mused on the way home. He decided he would have to ask some questions.

He had no notions on how to approach the problem, so when he arrived home, he asked for some basic information with the intention of introducing more advanced questions later, "How do you tell the difference between a boy and a girl?" he asked his mother. He knew the answer already, but reasoned that he could test the accuracy of the reply by posing a question the answer to which he knew.

Mrs Gabbett did not look up from her work at the kitchen table, "If you give a bar of soap each to a boy and a girl, and tell them to wash their hands, the boy will wash as far as his wrists, but a girl will wash as far as her elbows."

Gabriel pursued the matter no further, and like so many of his time and type, there was nothing more he could do but contain his curiosity and hope for the best. He used the ointment but the spots, pimples, lumps and pusy sores kept returning in crops until eventually he just gave up. They got no worse, and he suffered them and the effect they had on his morale for many a day to come.

If school had any redeeming feature for Gabriel it was that, though sport was declared to be compulsory, the enthusiasm for it on the part of the authorities was not excessive. The boys were expected to turn out for rugby once a week but, if a boy did not take part, no one seemed to mind, and Gabriel confined his appearances on the field to the warmer, drier days. He did, however, like playing games against other schools, not so much for the joy of playing, but for the fairly liberal quantities of tea and fruit cake which were provided at the end of these matches. He was not a good rugby player, and on occasions when a visiting team arrived short of one or two "men" he was detailed off to "volunteer" to play for the other side. This was considered to be a sporting gesture and in that sense and in his innocence, Gabriel always did his best for them. It was many years before it dawned on him why he had been chosen. He thought at the time that he was offered because, as sportsmen, his schoolmates would give up one of their average or even better players, rather than their worst, but he was wrong, he really was their worst. In all the games he ever played he never scored a try or kicked a goal. He was never even successful in getting a ball away from a scrum. He was never chosen to kick a penalty or to try for a conversion, even if the position was right in front of the posts, he was always the one to be told to lie prone to support the ball for some one else to kick. If The Beak's marking system had included rugby as a subject, he would have been awarded a further three or even two every week, even when he played for another school.

Sometimes he was chosen as a substitute, he was "A N Other" more than anyone else, and acted as touch-judge if not required to play. Gradually he became a permanent touch-judge and gained in three ways: he fulfilled the obligation to appear weekly on the playing field, he was able to remain fully clothed complete with overcoat and he qualified for the tea and fruit cake.

Despite being unhappy at school, Gabriel was far from being unhappy outside it, and during the longer days and holidays he found plenty to do.

He rode all over Dublin on his bicycle, his favourite place being dockland along the Liffey. He spent hours watching colliers negotiating the locks into the Grand Canal, and followed their progress across the dock to the quay where giant grabs lifted the coal from the ships and dumped it into hoppers in clouds of dust. He was spellbound and rather frightened by the dark dust-encrusted gasworks' dungeons as he looked down through large ventilating grills on the men labouring far below street level. How could any one exist in such a place of gloom, dust, smoke and roar?

He returned home by way of Britain Quay, where the Grand Canal enters the Dodder, to watch fish being unloaded from the trawlers *Tom Moore* and *Father O'Flynn* and the ice being poured down chutes into the holds. He crossed the three locks at the end of the canal, treading the narrow wooden walkways with the bicycle on one shoulder. At Ballsbridge he joined The Ramparts, a wide footway leading to Donnybrook,which runs between Johnson, Mooney & O'Brien's bakery and Herbert Park on one side and the Dodder on the other, sometimes stopping to watch a new horse being trained for the bakery delivery vans in a ring overlooking the river. Tiring of this he kept a lookout for kingfishers on the river bank as he rode home for his tea.

A prolonged tram strike resulted in the appearance of army lorries to transport the public on several routes across the city and out to the suburbs. These lorries provided an opportunity not to be missed: travel was free, and no questions asked. Gabriel lined up with the rest, got on board and stayed there until the end of the route was reached. He got off, walked around for an hour or so and then boarded another lorry to visit somewhere else. He liked best of all to go to Phoenix Park particularly if he had enough money to visit the zoo. Just inside the entrance a small compound was home to a few bedraggled American bison who stood motionless staring at the ground as if their horns were too heavy to bear. A penny put in the elephant's trunk bought a tin plate of bread chunks which the elephant ate and when it was finished it took the plate to return with the penny to its keeper, I don't see why I should have to pay to feed their bloody elephant, thought Gabriel as he set off to the monkey house where there might be something interesting to witness. I wonder why chimps have their bums inside-out?

Sometimes the soldiers organised sing-songs, many of the words parodies of the popular songs of the moment. To the air of "Roll Along Covered Wagon," they sang:

Will you come to Abyssinia, will you come?
Bring your own ammunition and your gun.
Mussolini will be there,
There'll be bullets in the air.
Will you come to Abyssinia, will you come?

Gabriel's increasing mobility enabled him to see more of his grandfather. He cut the Old Man's lawn on Sundays in the summer and so earned himself enough to go to the cinema every week. Sometimes he was given a book as well. One of these contained extracts from the diaries of explorers in Africa: Speke, Stanley, Livingstone. Gabriel was greatly impressed by their adventures, and formed the idea that he would get to Africa too. Mr Gabbett voiced the hope he would follow in his footsteps and go into a bank. This did not upset Gabriel; he had no hard views on the subject and was quite relieved to have this decision made for him. It was agreed that he would be better occupied at a commercial college studying the subjects required by the banks rather than at school, and so he found himself on his last day there with a note for The Beak informing him of his departure forthwith. Gabriel left the school in a state of elation. He said good-bye to no one and he never saw any of them again.

A few days later the Old Man died in his sleep. They followed his coffin to Mount Jerome cemetery, and as the grave was being filled in Gabriel was thinking of the advice he always got on his birthdays as the Old Man gave him his present: "As you grow older, may you grow wiser and be a better boy."

When the gravediggers had finished Mr Gabbett said, "Well there you are then," and putting his arm on Gabriel's shoulder led him away saying, "Let the earth lie lightly on him."

About this time, Gabriel joined the Air Raid Precautions Service in response to a recruiting notice in a shop window. He attended a course of lectures in a building in College Street to learn the duties of an air raid warden. He studied how to identify poison gases and what to do in the event of a gas attack, how to deal with unexploded bombs (leave them for the Army) and incendiaries (tackle them with a water spray and sand). At the end of his training he was ordered to report to the group warden who was to be found in the basement of a convent in Camden Street on Thursday evenings. The area was not rich. Gabriel had no idea what the unemployment rate was, but discovered that two out of three of his colleagues were out of work. This was the first time Gabriel came to know a significant number of poor people. They were all older than he was and all but a few had families to support.

As a warden, the first job he had was assembling gas-masks in the Round Room of the Mansion House, and later he had to issue them at sessions in the Kevin Street public library. One evening there was a rumour that a bomb had been dropped somewhere in Dun Laoghaire. The group warden telephoned the area headquarters in Tara Street but could not get confirmation of the event. He then rang up a friend in Dun Laoghaire who told him there had indeed been a bomb. "There's a bloody great hole in the road at the entrance to Rosmeen Gardens," he said.

So the rumour was true. Now that a real bomb had actually fallen, even though it was miles away, it changed everything. No longer were they living in a fantasy world of imaginary incidents and theoretical exercises: they had been attacked.

The group warden ordered everyone to report to the basement and told them that they were now to consider themselves to be on a war footing. This meant they would be expected to spend more time at the post, and that it would be staffed all night.

There was no trouble with manpower as hardly anyone had a job anyway, and being in the post with at least three others provided the opportunity to play solo in warm surroundings, which was better than staying in a cold home or leaning against a wall.

Mrs Gabbett did not like the idea of Gabriel's staying out all night but Mr Gabbett regarded the whole affair as a huge joke and gained endless amusement from the vision of Gabriel and a few wardens providing protection to the locality. He did not know them though. They were men and women less fortunate than the Gabbetts who found themselves in a depressed and depressing State which, though not long established, and lacking financial aid from any outsiders, succeeded in surviving.

Gabriel and the others joked about the "war footing," fully realising how nearly ridiculous they were with nothing but a helmet, a gas-mask and a pair of rubber boots. Each post in the group had a stirrup pump but only the one in Camden Street had a telephone and it had a lock on the dial to prevent misuse. The key was held by the group warden and he delegated its possession to no one so that even if the post had filled with enemy soldiers, this intelligence could not be passed on.

The excitement died down after a few days, but vigilance was not relaxed and some time later three of the other wardens and Gabriel were playing cards with the table pulled close to the fire. There was The Major, a small, stocky man with bright red hair who had gained his nickname as a result of his efforts to drill a collection of runners who were part of the organisation and were officially designated Emergency Communication Boys or ECBs. Some of these "boys" were older than Gabriel and resented the fact that he was a warden and they were not. Not all of them had been issued with helmets as there were not enough to go round, and this caused further resentment. On one occasion Gabriel had lent his helmet to one of them, who sat with it on his head for the rest of the night and when Gabriel asked for its return he was told to "piss off," on the grounds that as he had had the use of it for several weeks, it was now someone else's turn to have it. Feeling righteously indignant at suffering the deprivation of the helmet, but more so at being so rudely dismissed, Gabriel threatened a charge of insubordination if it were not handed over at once.

You can report what you like," snarled the boy, "I'm keepin' the hat."

At this stage The Major, who had overheard the row, intervened. "Give him back the helmet," he ordered, "or bejasus, I'll see to it yeh'll never get a message to carry."

At this the young man tore off the helmet, flung it at Gabriel and shouted as he left the post. "You can keep your bloody messages and I'm not comin' back."

The next card player was Charley. He was in his mid twenties, and one of the mainstays of the group, always cheerful, without the resigned air of depression which affected the older men.

The fourth player was Frank. He was in his late forties and had not had a job for years. He was pale and sickly, an aspect accentuated because he had lost nearly all his teeth. He carried a small scissors which he used to clip loose threads from the cuffs of his jacket where the fold had given way. He was the post patriarch and always seemed concerned at the use of foul language by the others, usually saying, "Now men, not in front of the lads," but this never prevented his shouting "Shit" when one of his cards was trumped.

They had been playing for several hours when there was the sound of an explosion rolling towards them.

"Thunder," Frank said, "play on."

"No, it bloody isn't," cried Charley as he dived for the door and clambered up the iron steps to street level, the others following closely behind him until all four stood huddled together on the little metal platform at the top.

"Shut up and listen," Charley commanded before anyone had said a word.

They listened in the bitterly cold January night watching small pools of light from the cowled street lamps reflecting the snow on the road.

They listened and shivered. They could hear the sound of an aeroplane quite far away.

"I told you," Charley said, "it's a bloody bomb."

"Where do you think it was?" someone asked.

"We'll have to wait until someone tells us."

By this time heads were appearing at windows and a few people shouted to know what had happened. They could say nothing except that they thought a bomb had been dropped somewhere. A reply which brought rude remarks and expressions of doubt about their usefulness.

Three of them went to the telephone box at Kelly's Corner, leaving The Major to stand by at the post in case a call came through on the phone there. They rang up Area Headquarters in Tara Street, but though the duty officer had heard the explosion, he did not know where it had occurred. At this stage, Frank suggested they call the fire brigade at Tara Street on the sound premise that someone from the area where the bomb had fallen would have asked them first for help. They got the answer that the bomb had dropped along the South Circular Road not far from Griffith Barracks.

Back at the post several other wardens had reported for duty. The group warden ordered everyone to his or her station. "Make sure the people see you, walk about until daylight, then you can go home. Be back here at 1900 hours."

When they arrived the following evening they were told the post was to be staffed twenty-four hours a day until further notice, and as things were now happening, the man in charge would be allowed to have the key to the telephone. This brought home to them the seriousness of the situation. They were to do a survey of their beats to find out the number of people in each house and the names of children who might have to be evacuated to the country. They made sketch maps of the district, marking the positions of hydrants and any special fire hazards such as petrol stations and wood-yards.

It was 1941 and the twenty-fifth anniversary of the declaration of the Irish Republic outside the

General Post Office in 1916 was coming near. It was to be commemorated by a parade of the defence forces and the auxiliary services on Easter Sunday. In preparation for this the group warden decided they must learn to march so that they could acquit themselves with dignity on the day, and for this purpose The Major was detailed off to be training officer.

In a local schoolyard he tried to get them to form fours, turn about, mark time, and generally go through a series of drill movements which would have taxed the ability of an elite infantry battalion. After several evenings of this, he gave up, "Jasus, fellas," he said, "yez'll never get it. Yez'll have to form fours here and join the parade as best yeh can. Then yez'll only have to stop and start an' mark time. Just try to keep a straight line and yer eyes front, an' yez'll be all right."

On the day, they joined the parade behind the Army and the other services, at the bottom of South Great George's Street. They marched past the Post Office with pride if not style and felt that if the Republic did not survive many more such celebrations it would not be their fault.

* * *

Gabriel responded well to the freedom of the college but despite his hard work, he did not go into a bank; something better happened which was to determine the course of his life.

He got to know other boys and girls studying for university entrance, including some intended for medical school. I'll become a doctor was a thought which came to him as he walked home along St Stephen's Green, that's what I'll do, I'll be a bloody doctor.

When Mr Gabbett heard the idea he was not very impressed, but nevertheless agreed that Gabriel could leave the college and go to a tutor or grinder to try for the entrance examination to the Royal College of Surgeons. Gabriel went to see Mr McDowell who had a room on the first floor of a tenement house behind the college in York Street. He opened the door to Gabriel who told him what he wanted to do. "Well you've come to the right place. Call me Mac. Do you know what you have to do?"

"Yes, I've got the syllabus. I think I can manage the geography and the French, but I'm not so hot in maths and I've never read the set English books."

"You'll have to know bloody *Hamlet* backwards."

"I can do it. When can I start?"

"Go and get the books together and be back here in the morning, ten sharp."

There were ten or twelve other students in Mac's class. They spent the weeks before the examination going through *Hamlet* repeatedly, learning by heart all the important speeches, discovering the meaning of difficult passages and preparing studies of all the characters from Hamlet to "Rosie and Guildie," as Mac called the messengers. They revised the mathematics course, studied French verbs and practised translations. "Never mind the bloody pronunciation," Mac advised them, "there's no oral." They drew maps and analysed Addison. At the end of it all, Gabriel passed: he was now a medical student.

"You'll be able to take care of us all soon," Mr Gabbett told him when he handed over the cheque for the college fees.

Gabriel felt his father's confidence well-placed, if a little premature. He would be learning something of value, not wasting hours chanting the order of liturgical colours or the details of clerical vestments but something more to do with the reality of all about him.

***

Sex began with a wet-dream. Nothing odd about that but it frightened the life out of Gabriel when he awoke to find he had wet the bed. In the middle of the night he had to rinse out his pyjama trousers in the bath, and tell his mother in the morning that they had accidently fallen in the water. He was very upset at what had happened and was worried he might have some disease which made his urine thick but as he felt quite well he decided to do nothing and in a few days stopped being concerned about the event. His relief was short-lived, for a week later the same thing happened again, only this time he woke up just before it started and experienced the sensations of orgasm for the first time. He placed the wet pyjama trousers under his pillow and hoped his mother would not notice them.

He was very puzzled about the whole business, but suffering no ill-effect, he awaited developments. He had no alternative, there was nothing he could do. He could not face the thought of going to the doctor about such an embarrassing occurrence. He determined however to take a simple precaution: he put a handkerchief in his pyjama pocket. Nothing happened for several nights until he awakened to grab his penis to control the flow, but this only made it happen faster. He was successful in avoiding messing up his pyjamas again and felt he had won a little victory. He wiped himself dry and lay awake thinking of what to do next. Before settling down to go to sleep again he got another handkerchief and held it around his penis which in a short time became enlarged and started to throb. He found holding it so pleasant, he rubbed it up and down, and in seconds had another orgasm. This was a great relief for he now knew what to do to prevent wetting the bed, but at the same time awful and terrifying thoughts commanded his attention.

Things he had heard from the priests at school about impurity crossed his mind. He realised what the doctor had meant about bad habits and touching himself "down there." So this is what it is all about, he thought, this is impurity. He remembered what he had been told about all sins of impurity being serious matter, so there were only the other two conditions to be fulfilled to make this a mortal sin: there had to be full consent and full knowledge. Well, he had had free will in the action, but he had not had full knowledge: he had not known what he was doing until after he had done it. Thank God, he thought, that was a near thing. He had not committed a mortal sin, and of course he would not in the future.

He felt quite pleased about the whole incident after this; he had made a discovery of the nature of mortal sin without outside help. This is what the undefined impurity was all about: it meant playing with your tool. Why could they not have said so? That reproduction was associated in any way with it never occurred to him. He was totally uninformed about any aspect of the physiology of reproduction, and even if he had been told the truth, it is more than likely that he would not have believed it, such was the power of the conditioning he had undergone. Later, the association of ejaculation and reproduction became clear to him, though it did so only gradually as he pieced together scattered fragments of information, some gleaned by chance reading, but most by hearing dirty stories, the only form of sex education available at the time in Dublin.

Two nights after discovering the meaning of impurity he awoke again. What was he to do? He tried lying quietly with the handkerchief in place in the hope of going back to sleep, but his penis just throbbed all the more. He tried praying as he had been instructed to do at times of temptation. He said three Hail Marys but there was no change, and eventually he did it again. He had committed a mortal sin, if he died before he could get to confession he would be damned for all eternity. He was guilty of a sin that kills the soul. At least that was what the pious priests had told him. It was to be years before the whole matter was placed in the category of human habits where it belonged and not in the lists of sins, manufactured shadows of a non-existent substance. The problem at the time, however, was deadly serious for Gabriel.

He awoke in the morning grateful to find he was still alive. He had not died in the night. He had been given another chance, and now his one thought was to get to confession as quickly as possible to be purged of his evil. He had to decide where to go. He could not go to any priest who might recognise him. His shame at being known as a person in mortal sin was more than he could face.

Gabriel normally went to confession about once a month. The story was always the same: "Bless me Father for I have sinned," he would say, leaning his forehead against the grill separating him from the priest.

The priest mumbled something in Latin, then asked, "How long is it since your last confession?"

"A month Father."

"Go on."

"I told lies, I took Our Lord's name in vain." This meant he had said "Bejasus" or "Christ" in a profane context. It was all right to say "Begod," because the commandment said: "Thou shalt not take the name of the Lord, thy God in vain," and the name in question was "Jesus Christ", not "God." "God" was not a name, "God" was God.

"I used bad language," meaning he had said "damn" or "blast,"; "bloody" did not count.

He finished by saying, "For these and all the other sins of my past life I am very sorry."

"For your penance say three Hail Marys. O my God...."

This was the signal for Gabriel to say the act of contrition and, as he recited it, the priest uttered the words of absolution in Latin, and then added, "God bless you," as he closed the shutter between them.

Apart from waiting-time for his turn to come, the whole operation took less than two minutes.

There were over a dozen churches within a radius of a mile of the Gabbetts', and after consideration, Gabriel decided to go to the Carmelites in Whitefriar Street where several confessors were usually in attendance, none of them acquainted with him. One in particular was there throughout nearly the whole day. He always had the largest number of people waiting to go to him, even if several other priests were there; and he was fast, even by Dublin standards. Gabriel doubted if the average time from start to finish exceeded a minute. He had never been to him before, having been put off by the numbers waiting, but he had heard of him as a man who dealt with "hard chaws and chancers." He was not sure what this meant in terms of confession, but he knew all right that this was the category of sinner to which he now belonged. The priest was Father Devlin. He was an old man with a red nose and a shock of white hair which stood up in a quiff over his forehead. He walked slowly and with difficulty, and seemed to suffer with backache. Gabriel had considered some of the other priests, but decided in the end that Father Devlin was the one. He took his place at the end of the queue of people waiting, and carefully prepared himself as he moved ever closer to the confessional. He debated with himself whether to go straight into the mortal sin and get it over with or to rattle off the usual venial sins and then mention the big one. He chose the latter course. Eventually his turn came. He knelt before the grill anxious, embarrassed and filled with remorse. Father Devlin opened the door covering the grill and, as his face appeared asked, "How long is it since your last confession?" before Gabriel could request his blessing or tell him he had sinned.

"Ten days Father bless me Father for I have sinned," he gabbled.

"Well?"

"Father, I told lies, I took the Lord's name in vain; I used bad language."

"Just blurted it out?"

"Yes Father."

"Anything else?"

"And Father."

"Yes?"

"I had impure thoughts, Father."

"But you put them away from you?"

Gabriel nearly agreed, to grasp at a way out, but he knew it would only make matters worse.

"No Father. I was impure," in a choked whisper.

"How many times?"

"Once, Father."

"Anything else?"

"For these and all the other sins of my past life I am very sorry."

"For your penance say the rosary. O my God...."

"O my God I am heartily sorry for having offended Thee...," started Gabriel.

"God bless you," said Father Devlin, and was gone.

Gabriel clambered out of the box feeling he had been there for ages, and that all eyes were on him. I can't have been kept longer than anyone else, he thought, with doubtful assurance. He considered a whole rosary to be a bit severe. Carefully done it would take at least ten minutes, but he did not mind. It was a small price to pay. He was back in the fold. He felt like the Prodigal Son returned home; like the single lost sheep back with the herd. He loved Father Devlin and everyone else. He loved the church for providing this escape from hell for him, but he never realised that if it had not been for the professional virgins who ran it, he would never have been in such a guilt-ridden state in the first place. That revelation was many years and many more "mortlers" in the future.

But for now, all was well. He had sinned, confessed, repented, resolved not to sin again and was about to perform his penance. He had been forgiven by God. From now on life would be easier. He had fallen but had overcome his difficulty. He had been to the gates of hell and returned. What else was there to fear?

His peace of mind was short-lived, for before the end of the week he was faced with the same problem as before, and had to go through the whole performance again.

The trouble continued to recur and brought with it an extra dimension—frequency. How many manipulations could he allow himself before Father Devlin finally lost patience with such blatant sinning? He always asked Gabriel how many times he had been impure if he did not volunteer the information on completing the recitation of his faults.

He decided he must find a new confessor, not instead of Father Devlin, but in addition to him. He visited several churches to check on the numbers outside the various confessionals and eventually chose Father Conleth in the Carmelite church in Clarendon Street. He had seen in the porch a notice reading: "Watch your Handbag," and this public and practical recognition of human frailty gave him confidence and helped in making his decision.

Father Conleth was satisfactory, but not so calm, quiet and reassuring as Father Devlin, and he too asked how many times the offence had been committed. He was good enough though to be visited again if necessary, even if he was a little terse.

Gabriel could never understand why each priest insisted on knowing the precise number of times the sin was committed. It never made any difference to the length or style of the short homily he often received on the efficacy of asking the Blessed Virgin to intercede with her Son to help him overcome his failings, nor to the penance given: it was always the rosary. He knew that one mortal sin was enough to qualify for certain eternal damnation; so, that he was damned more than once was neither here nor there.

The intervals between confessions became a problem. He could not really go more often than once a week, for this would have labelled him as a completely incorrigible sinner. So it became apparent that he needed more confessors who could be depended upon not to attack him or even send him to the bishop for absolution. He acquired two more: Dr O'Brien at the University Church and an Oblate father in Inchicore. The church there has an imitation Lourdes grotto in the grounds with a life size statue of the Immaculate Conception. This enabled him to say his penance and make his supplications to the Blessed Virgin as a single exercise. There were now four priests on Gabriel's roster which meant that he was able to visit each one only once a month thus reducing the chances that any one of them might remember him and decide to attack him for his failure to overcome his evil ways. The fear, remorse and guilt affected his behaviour to such an extent that when he was in "a state of mortal sin" he thought of little else. No wonder Dr Tom asked me if I have any dirty habits, he thought. This is what he meant. No wonder I have acne. Not only am I killing my soul I am damaging my body as well by causing these awful spots and blemishes, and contributing to the physical as well as the spiritual destruction of my body, the Temple of the Holy Ghost.

If he had to cross the road he was in constant fear of being killed in an accident. He rode his bicycle with infinite care, saying decades of the rosary as he pedalled along in anticipation of the penance he would be given, and he said extra prayers pleading that this terrible carnal lust be removed from him to allow him to lead a normal life like anyone else. Though he did not know it that was just what he was doing.

How bloody ridiculous it all seemed to him years later but what agonies of mind he suffered at the time! After each confession he was always as filled with relief at the end as he was of fear at the beginning. His feelings of remorse gradually faded away and guilt only died a long time later as he, rather belatedly, entered manhood and began to allow his own reason to take over from the conditioning and highly developed barriers to knowledge carefully established and nurtured by the great conspiracy maintained by the society which reared him.

Gabriel noticed, after some months, that the acne, rather than becoming worse, improved and eventually disappeared. He put this down to the power of prayer, and determined more than ever that as God had granted him a cure he must redouble his efforts to overcome his terrible habit, but fortunately, he never did.

Chapter 3

Gabriel's life in the College of Surgeons began with an introduction to the Schools of Surgery by the superintendent, a lugubrious man who lectured the students on the subjects of diligence and punctuality. "You're on the threshold of a career in an honourable profession," he told them, "and you are expected to conduct yourselves accordingly. You're no longer children; you are getting an education that is the envy of all, and, believe you me when I tell you, I'll stand no nonsense from anyone who doesn't behave."

Gabriel did behave and, at the end of his first year, following days at lectures and practical classes, and nights in study, he took his examinations in chemistry, physics and biology, and passed them all.

The social life was very limited. There was no students' residence, and they either lived at home or in digs. Gabriel and his friends had coffee every day in the back basement of Roberts' in Grafton Street, a place presided over by a Miss Courtenay who ruled supreme and stood no nonsense from any student tending to be boisterous. The café was also popular with shoppers and business people, and the proprietors provided a trio of mature ladies to entertain their customers with Strauss and Léhar waltzes and selections of musical gems from *The Mikado* and other light works. They played with a gusto and application that would have done credit to the Berlin Philharmonic but few paid any attention to them. No one ever applauded when they galloped, often together, to the end of a foot-tapping polka; they just spoke less loudly until the good ladies restarted with undiminished vigour.

At the end of his second year Gabriel passed the examination in anatomy and physiology, and as these were considered to be the hardest of the whole course, he felt that from that point things would be easier. Following his summer holiday he began his clinical work. The system allowed a student to attend any of the teaching hospitals, and it became Gabriel's custom to go to those in which his examiners worked. Sometimes he went on the ward rounds of other doctors or professors if he considered them to be particularly good or if they did not start too early in the mornings.

One venerable, very ancient and popular physician at Baggot Street hospital was noted for not asking his students questions, so one could attend in the knowledge that reveries would go undisturbed and ignorance unexposed. He had the irritating habit though of allowing his voice to rise when he had something important to say but then of dropping it to a whisper when he came to the vital point, thus allowing only the student right beside him to hear it. Gabriel had one of these pearls imparted to him alone when the old man grabbed him by the arm and shouted, "Now this is a most important point," and then in a whisper, just beside his ear, "take the patient's temperature"—long pause—"with a thermometer."

Despite their idiosyncrasies, or maybe because of them, his teachers succeeded in instilling in Gabriel the desire and ability to learn, and this he did, but at the same time he never lost sight of his need for leisure which he met by regular visits to Neary's in Chatham Street.

Money was always a problem. He had no regular allowance from his father but his mother gave him a few shillings and his Uncle Henry provided him with half-a-crown every Saturday.

Henry was Mrs Gabbett's bachelor brother who lived with their aunt in Sandycove. He was a commercial traveller for jams, chocolate, sweets of all sorts and, according to season, Easter eggs and Christmas stockings. He spent the working week visiting shops in counties Kerry, Clare and Limerick, and returned to Dublin on Friday evenings. His passion was backing horses. There was a bookmaker's shop, or Turf Accountant, as he styled himself, a few doors from the Gabbetts', and Gabriel spent most of Saturday afternoons going to and fro with betting slips or bookies' tickets, but hardly ever with any winnings. There was no worse judge of a horse's chances than Uncle Henry, and despite meticulous study of form in the *Irish Field*, he seldom if ever had a winner. He usually bet a maximum of half-a-crown each way even on a "certainty," and only race by race, giving Gabriel the betting slip and money for each race, pronouncing a blessing as he did so waving his hand like a priest, "In the name of the Ace, King and Queen of Diamonds, may this horse come home ahead of all the others and not be running unto life everlasting, Amen." Then Gabriel went to the decrepit and filthy shop to await his turn in line to give away the money. On one occasion there was such a crowd that he could not get the bet on before the start of the race. The horse lost and he found himself with an easy five shillings. This gave him the idea of covering the bets himself and when he told Mrs Gabbett of his plan, she agreed to help out in the event of the worst happening—a long-shot winner coming up.

However, there was more to Henry than a liking for gambling. He was a tall heavily-built man with a large oval jovial face which advertised his personality. He was a man who could extract humour from any situation; laughter surrounded him like a crowd. His standard greeting on holding out his hand was, "Bonjourno cascara sagrada," which he claimed was Spanish for "Good day, may you never have to run for it."

He fashioned his behaviour on the music-hall comedians of his youth, and his ability to reminisce on past events with an appropriate comic anecdote was limitless. The young Gabbetts never doubted their veracity even though he claimed, "You should never let the truth ruin a good story."

Viewed from behind, he resembled the back legs of an elephant. He wore dark grey made-to-measure suits, but always looked baggy and lumpy. The latter was the case particularly as he was in the habit of carrying pots of jam or boxes of chocolates in especially commodious pockets he ordered when he "had a suit built," as he expressed it himself. He did imitations: standing in the centre of the room with his arms by his sides he slowly revolved where he stood with eyes and mouth tightly shut until he completed a circle, then he opened eyes and mouth wide and said, "Tuskar Rock Lighthouse on a clear night." Another favourite was the "drunken sailor looks out to sea," which consisted of standing to gaze out the window with his hand, palm downwards on the back of his head to provide shade, as he recited,

'Twas a dirty night and a low-down trick
When our ship turned turtle in the At-lan-tic.
The sea was as smooth as a baby's bottle.
There wasn't a policeman in sight.
Even the sardines turned over in their tins
And pulled up the lid for the night.

Henry was Gabriel's confidant. They talked on all topics and, though they often disagreed, they had a rapport which protected them from acrimony. Gabriel's poor school reports were often discussed, but on seeing a particularly bad one, Henry would say, "They never gave me a report at all, but what the hell. Any bloody fool can be bottom in a subject or two, but it takes real genius to be as lousy as you."

On saying this he did a short elephantine tap-dance and sang the chorus of "The Man who broke the Bank at Monte Carlo," and when he was finished announced in ringing tones as if addressing a full house, "And now Mr Jemser Byrne will give us a few bars of a song."

Then in an aside, "What are you going to sing Jemser?"

Assuming a lugubrious air: "De Rosary."

"Silence now please, Ladies and Gentlemen. One voice only. Mr Jemser Byrne will render 'The Rosary,' Jasus Mary an' Joseph," and he burst into gales of laughter.

A month before Gabriel was due to do his hospital residence, Henry suffered a heart attack. Gabriel went to see him in hospital, and though he was only a fourth-year medical student with very limited clinical experience, it was obvious to him Henry was dying. He was propped up, and had the grey-blue pallor of a dying life.

The next day he seemed a little better and quite chatty. Gabriel told him of how, in a recent poker game, he had not seen a highish bet though he was holding three aces.

"Jasus," gasped Henry, "I wouldn't have gone with two. Christ, never drop out with three aces."

These were the last words to pass between them; in a few hours he was dead.

They all went to see him for the last time in the hospital mortuary. He was in his coffin holding a rosary to his breast and enveloped in a white shroud. He had had something to say about shrouds in the past, "The bloody shrouds they make nowadays are useless; you'd wear the back out of one in a week. It doesn't matter for bishops though, they bury them standing up to give them a head start on the rest of us when the final bugle blows."

Well, here he was, in one himself, thought Gabriel, and the vision of his laughing in heaven made tears trickle down his cheeks. How could this be dear old Henry in such a humiliating situation? It must be one of his gags, any minute now he will jump up, do a little tap-dance, holding his hands under his chin, and sing:

"I'm Nellie O'Grady the Two-headed Lady,
I ain't got no body, nobody but me."

They followed the coffin to St Michael's Church in Dun Laoghaire and the next day to Deans Grange Cemetery. It was a sunny August day.

Memories of Henry remained with Gabriel. If anything untoward or funny happened his first thought was to tell him, only instantly to realise he was no longer there. He thought of how he would have been pleased at his progress, and of how he would have laughed to know how his Saturday bets had been covered, based on the knowledge that he was the world's worst punter. Above all he remembered his presence, his joviality, his gift for bringing gaiety, and his silly, corny jokes that never failed: that was because they loved each other. If trouble came, there was even a verse to cover that eventuality:

The world will never adjust itself
To suit your plans to the letter.

Things will go wrong your whole life long,
And the sooner you know it, the better.

* * *

Gabriel was chronically short of money and, as he got older, he developed more expensive tastes, like eating out rather than going home for meals; so another source of income had to be found: he started pawning his books. This did not help very much but it was fashionable among medical students.

The nearest pawnshop to the college was Meredith's in Cuffe Street. Like any other shop it was divided into two parts by a counter, but unlike an ordinary shop this one had a wire mesh, supported by vertical brass poles separating the two sections. At the lower end of the mesh there was a gap running the length of the counter which enabled a customer to push in the article to be pledged, while preventing the assistant from being exposed to an unacceptable risk of assault. At the back of the shop were small cubicles with doors which provided some privacy for those reluctant to carry on business in the public gaze, but there was no surer way of attracting attention than to use one of these "confessionals."

The pawnbroker was a sickly, thin cadaverous man named Mick, who despite his appearance and the delicacy of his position remained in the best of spirits.

The students avoided pawning anything on Fridays or Mondays, because on these days many people were either taking the weekend clothing out or putting it back in, and with the place crowded it was difficult to spend time haggling over a few extra pence for a book. On Gabriel's first visit he took his Gray's *Anatomy* to raise money for a party. The book was not an up-to-date edition but it had been well kept: he had paid twelve shillings for it secondhand. Unlike most medical books, this one tended to hold its value. He handed the book to Mick who asked how much he wanted on it.

"Ten bob," answered Gabriel.

"Ah go away! What do yeh think I am? I'll give yeh half-a-dollar."

Gabriel drew himself back from the counter, waved a hand at the book and said with a hurt air, "Get away Mick. It's in bloody good condition, and I'll be getting it out again."

"That's what they all say," retorted Mick. "Half-a-dollar, and I have twenty more of the fuckin' things above in the store."

"Well I'll take three bob," said Gabriel with resignation.

"Yeh bloody well won't. Yeh'll take two an' nine, and consider yerself lucky I'm in a good mood today."

Mick took the book away to a high desk where he filled in the pawn ticket, writing with a steel-nibbed pen and India ink and dipping the completed paper in a small box of sawdust. He gave the ticket and the money to Gabriel.

As Gabriel turned to go a woman appeared at the door of the shop hauling behind her an old broken-down pram which contained something covered with a black shawl. She came towards the counter.

"We're not takin' prams Missus," said Mick, banging the counter with the flat of his hand.

"I'm not hockin' the pram."

"What have yeh, then?"

"I'll show yeh in there," she replied, heading for one of the cubicles.

"Ah yeh don't need to go in there," said Mick. "This gentleman won't mind seein' what yeh have."

She had reached the door of the "confessional" but the pram was too wide to go through, so she had to accept the lack of privacy and return to the counter. She removed the shawl to reveal a two-foot high plaster statue of St Patrick, complete with departing snakes at the feet, a shamrock in one hand and a bishop's crozier in the other.

"Oh God forgive yeh, Missus," cried Mick in mock horror, "yeh can't hock that."

"Well I must," replied the woman, "and I want a quid for it. It's the only way I'll ever get any money outa St Patrick. He doesn't listen to me prayers."

"Two bob," offered Mick.

"Make it ten," she countered. "It was a weddin' present, and I'll be gettin' it out next week."

"Nothing doing. Half-a-dollar, take it or leave it Missus."

"All right then," she sighed, and heaved the statue on to the counter assisted by Gabriel.

"I don't think statues are any good at all," she went on, "I've been prayin' for years for a winner off of St Francis down in Clarendon Street but nothin' ever comes up."

"Yer usin' the wrong one. That's the small one for the dogs. Yeh need the big one at Adam and Eve's; that's for the horses," declared Mick with great authority and went on, "Did yeh hear they're goin' to take Nelson off the Pillar an' put up St Patrick instead?"

"No. Who told yeh that?" asked the woman.

"There was a man in here the other day was tellin' me," then turning to Gabriel asked, "Did you hear that Doc?"

"No I didn't," answered Gabriel, "and I don't believe it anyway."

"Well there might be some truth in it," said Mick, "it's about time they got him down. What did he ever do for Ireland?"

"Musha, as far as I'm concerned," exclaimed the woman, "they can put Jasus, Mary an' Joseph on it but it'll still be Nelson's Pillar."

Before Mick could comment further she went on, "I don't suppose yeh'd let us have five bob on the pram Mick?"

"Yer bloody right Missus, I wouldn't. I wouldn't give tuppence on it. It'd cost a shillin' just to store it for a week."

"Ah maybe it's just as well. I'll need it to bring home the statue again. I'd better be off, yer man'll be back for his tea."

She left followed by Gabriel and when they were on the pavement she asked him, "Are you one of the young doctors?"

"I am; why?"

"It's just boozin' money for you, hockin' books, but that statue means a few stone of coal for me."

Gabriel was about to say something when she stopped him, "I've seen you young fellas for years. When yez become proper doctors yez go away an' forget the likes of me."

Then before Gabriel could say anything and to his embarrassment and surprise, she touched her fingers to his cheek and said, "Don't forget me."

Turning from him, she adjusted the shawl over her head, and clasping it beneath her chin ambled off pushing the pram before her, leaving Gabriel staring after her with a hint of guilt in his heart.

***

With the passing years Gabriel's dreams of travelling to Africa never dimmed, and on gloomy days he cycled down the South Wall to the end of Sir John Rogerson's Quay to where the Dodder joins the Liffey, and sat on a bollard to gaze down the river towards the Pigeon House power station and the sea beyond. If he had time he went further, crossed the Grand Canal lock gates and the Dodder bridge at Ringsend, and rode along the Pigeon House Road following the track around the power station and on to the causeway towards the Poolbeg Lighthouse. He liked to sit with his back to it and think of the day he would leave, saying to himself, I'm going, by Christ I'm going. Some day, somehow, I'm going.

Why did he want so much to go? To travel? To see the world? These were the apparent reasons but deeper down he was aware of a dissatisfaction with his stagnant environment. I'll be a refugee from humbug and hypocrisy, he told himself.

During his training Gabriel was resident for part of the time in the Richmond Hospital where he worked in clinics and went on ward rounds, helped clerk in patients on admission and assisted at operations. He did periods in casualty and watched the pathologist performing post-mortems.

He lived for two months in the Rotunda Hospital to learn the practice of obstetrics. Apart from the facilities for patients in the hospital there was a domiciliary midwifery service staffed by the medical students.

Prior to starting at the Rotunda Gabriel had been given a list of the articles he would require to enable him to function: a pair of scissors, some string, a rubber apron and gloves, an artery forceps, a mucus catheter to clear babies' airways and a suitable bag to carry the lot. He took trouble to provide himself with everything but discovered later that the only essentials were a razor blade and a piece of string.

On arrival at the hospital Gabriel and his colleagues had to attend at least two normal deliveries in the labour ward, and then they would be allocated to a district team, each of which consisted of three students of whom at least one had been doing the work for a few weeks.

For three days after seeing two babies born nothing happened. The new students spent most of the time reading or lying around the lawns at the rear of the hospital. In the evenings they went to Conway's pub across the street, one of them going to the porter's lodge from time to time to find out if they had moved up on the on-call list, but it was early one morning before they reached the top. A porter came to call Gabriel who found his two comrades waiting for him at the lodge, "Where are we going?" he asked.

"Carnlough Road, West Cabra; the father's here to show us the way."

The father told them that this would be his third child, and apart from this piece of information said nothing further until their arrival at the house. He opened the door for them then rode off on his bicycle.

"So long," he said.

The students went upstairs to find the mother sitting up in bed smoking a cigarette. There was also another woman there wearing a white overall, and a black hat fixed to her head with a long pin which had at one end a red knob not much smaller than a billiard ball. She was the unofficial midwife, The Handywoman, who belonged to a tribe, members of which were to be found all over Dublin, who help at deliveries and who, though completely without formal training, had acquired over the years a profound experience of midwifery, and whose help to countless mothers and babies was inestimable. It would have been a foolish student who ignored their warnings of impending danger to a mother or baby.

Today's handywoman was small and thin, and looked very sickly. She greeted the students with a sad smile and said, "Good morning doctors, whicha yez is doin' it?"

"I am, Missus," answered Ian, the senior member of the team.

This had been arranged in advance, as the one with previous experience, he would deliver the baby while the others watched and made themselves useful.

"Yez'll have a wait," said the handywoman. "She still has her waters. I'll go down an' put on the kettle."

Ian had produced a notebook and he wrote down details of the mother's obstetric history. He recorded her temperature and pulse-rate, and determined the lie of the baby. He put his ear to her bulging belly to hear the baby's heart. All seemed well. The baby was in the correct position with its head well down in the pelvis. Gabriel and the other student took turns in listening to the foetal heart.

The handywoman returned carrying a tray with a pot of tea, some milk and sugar, cups and saucers, "We'll let it draw for a while," she said, adding, "Give me the things Doctor, an' I'll boil them for yeh."

Ian handed over rubber gloves, scissors and the forceps tied to a length of string. She took everything downstairs, and returned to pour out the tea.

They sat around talking about nothing in particular until the mother said she felt another pain coming on, the previous having been just before the arrival of the team.

"It's only a little one," announced the handywoman. "I told yez yeh'd have a long wait. Yer man had to go, he *had* to go, he couldn't wait a minute. He came for me at five o'clock an' said, 'I'm goin' for to get the doctors; you go round to the house,' but I made him come back with me, an' when I saw how long things would be I told him to leave it till nine or ten, but he wouldn't wait. 'I'm off for to get the doctors,' he said, an' nothin' could stop him."

As the morning wore on, the patient's contractions became more regular and intense, until at about eleven the handywoman declared, "The waters have gone. I'll go an' get the saucepan."

The mother lay placidly on her back. She had stopped smoking. The handywoman returned with the saucepan containing the rubber gloves and the instruments, with the end of the string dangling over the edge so that the forceps could be pulled out without contamination.

When the baby's arrival was judged to be imminent, Ian put on his apron and went to wash his hands, returning to fish out the rubber gloves with the forceps. He was now ready.

Obstetricians differ in their preferred methods of delivering babies. Some like the mother to lie on her back, others prefer her to lie on her left side. Rotunda custom dictated the latter: no one seems to have asked the mother. The operator stands to the mother's right to allow his left arm to pass on the inside of the raised right thigh which is supported in the air by an assistant. His right hand passes underneath, to allow for the manipulation of the baby's head as it appears.

This delivery was a short one and with the baby's arrival very near, the mother was encouraged by orders from the handywoman, "push," or "wait."

In fact she bore down or waited as her physiology demanded. The commands only seemed to be obeyed because they were skilfully kept in time, thus enhancing the handywoman's reputation as one "who knew her stuff."

When the baby was finally expelled in a flood of blood-stained fluid, Ian clamped the umbilical cord with the forceps and tied two pieces of string close together on it near the baby's navel, then he severed it with the scissors between the constrictions.

The baby was a girl, and it was Gabriel's job to hold her up by the heels as she gave a great gasping cry and started to breathe. He carried her to a table and laid her on a towel which he wrapped around her. She was a bluish-pink colour, covered in streaks of blood and soft waxy grease. He picked her up and laid her along his forearm with her head cradled in the palm of his hand. He wanted to say something by way of greeting, so bringing her face close to his, he whispered to her alone, "Hello little lady. Welcome to this Valley of Tears."

He placed the child beside the mother, "Well, here she is. Here's your daughter," he said.

The mother did not look around, she just said, speaking to the wall, "I don't give a damn if it's a mule, as long as I've got rid of it."

Half an hour after the birth the placenta had been expelled, the mother cleaned up and all made tidy, and the boys were on their way back to the hospital to await the next call.

On some occasions if they were detained by a slow labour, or if there were many births occurring at the same time, they could find themselves first on-call as soon as they returned to the hospital. This was very tiring, and often they slept in a chair or sitting on the floor leaning against a wall until things began to happen.

Throughout the period, despite the tiredness and squalor, the people they worked for always seemed so resigned to their lot that Gabriel often tried to discuss conditions with them, but he never got very far; he was told, "It's the Holy Will of God, Sir."

The families invariably managed to provide endless cups of tea and tomato sandwiches, no matter how poverty-stricken they seemed, and even if things went wrong, their care for the "doctors" never diminished.

If trouble during labour developed, it was usually the handywoman who knew it first. She would size up the situation, take the leader aside and suggest, "I think we'd better get the van."

The "van" was a blue stationwagon used to transport a doctor and an anaesthetist with specially packed sterile equipment. It was well-known all over the north of Dublin, and though its arrival at a house was not as dramatic as that of the fire brigade, it was none the less welcome in time of need. It was of pre-war vintage and none too reliable. It suffered from intermittent clutch trouble which caused it to have an irregular hesitancy of motion which earned it the name "Eclampsia," a word, borrowed from obstetrics, which is applied to a condition associated with maternal convulsions.

When skilled help became necessary one of the students cycled to the hospital to request it. This could have been done by telephone, but the student had to act as guide on the return journey as many of the doctors were strangers to Dublin.

On the night that Gabriel was due to assist at his last district delivery he had been to a party and got drunk, and while he and Ian were performing the Mexican Hat Dance on a table in the doctors' mess they were called to an address in Summerhill quite close to the hospital.

The house was a broken-down tenement from which the hall door had long disappeared. They went to a room on the first floor which in more elegant times had been a drawing-room but now housed a family of five. The mother was standing at the window overlooking the street. She was holding a tea-cup in one hand and rubbing her belly with the other.

As Gabriel entered the room he felt ill and immediately sat astride a chair, draping his arms on its back to cushion his head.

"Oh, get up," ordered Neil, the third student in the team. "You're supposed to be doing this delivery."

"So what," sighed Gabriel, "I'll be ready by the time she is," indicating the mother.

"Ah leave the poor fella alone," she said. "Can't yeh see he's had a hard night?"

"You're right, Missus," beamed Gabriel, "Would you like a bottle of stout?"

"Oh Jasus I'd love one. Yeh haven't got any, have yeh?"

"We're prepared for all emergencies," declared Gabriel taking a bottle and corkscrew from his bag. "Get yourself a glass."

She put down the cup to take a tumbler from a cupboard. Gabriel handed her the opened bottle.

"You shouldn't be doing that," Neil protested. "Alcohol is contraindicated in pregnancy."

"Rubbish," reasoned Gabriel. "One bottle of stout is not going to do her any harm."

"He's right," said the mother patting her front. "The night I got this I'd had nine."

They had to wait hours for the baby and, as they sat there, the mother related how she had been born in the same room during the Troubles. Her father had told her that he became mixed up in an incident involving police and troops and was taken to the Bridewell. No one would believe him when he claimed to be on his way to the hospital for the students. Meanwhile, her mother was left with the handywoman who eventually delivered her of the new baby, Gabriel's patient.

It did not seem to Gabriel that much had changed in the intervening years. The British had gone, but the slums remained.

"I wonder what things'll be like when this one grows?" the mother asked.

With the baby delivered, disconnected, induced to breathe, washed and wrapped, the students were on their way back to the Rotunda with the daily life of Dublin starting around them.

* * *

It was the start of Gabriel's last year at college. He was more mature, more knowledgeable but still the recipient only of what was available to him within the confines of a stultifying environment.

He knew—he never had any other idea—that achieving his qualification was to be his means of escape.

All his formal lectures were now finished. He was on his own, expected to be a regular attender at clinics and ward rounds, while at the same time studying for his final examinations: the big three—surgery, medicine, obstetrics. It was permissible to take each separately. He decided to do obstetrics first, as the one freshest in his mind.

All the examinations had three parts: a written paper, a clinical test consisting of examining patients and discussing their investigation and treatment, and finally an oral test. To be able to attempt all this with any hope of success, it was necessary to arrange an intensive routine so that the entire course could be read at least twice before concentrating on the most difficult and important parts.

Gabriel knew from experience how much time he would need. He reckoned on six weeks, not including Saturdays and Sundays. He arose at six each day and did a few hours' work before breakfast. He spent the rest of the day at clinics, studying at home or in the college library before having half an hour's break in the afternoon with his friends in Roberts' cafe.

Eventually, he paid the six guinea entrance fee, and when the day came, spent three hours writing pages of what he hoped was in accordance with his examiners' expectations. The following day he went back to the Rotunda for his clinical test. With this part of the examination completed, it was the custom for students to be told whether or not they should bother to attend for the oral, for if the clinical section was failed, the whole was failed. Gabriel was told to continue. Well, so far, so good, he thought, and he felt a quiet confidence.

The orals were held in the college council chamber, and the six candidates allotted the same period presented themselves in an anteroom. When Gabriel's turn came he went in and took the chair indicated by one of the examiners. He was asked several questions on a wide range of obstetrics and gynaecology, and finally one of the examiners pointed to a microscope on the table in front of Gabriel and said, "Take a look down that, and tell us what you see."

Gabriel looked down it, and was able to identify a section of the lining of a uterus. He had no idea what was wrong with it, but he did assume that there must be something wrong with it on the grounds that no examiner would be rotter enough to ask for a comment on a normal specimen under such circumstances. There's got to be something wrong with it, he thought. He moved the glass slide from side to side, and gazed in total ignorance at whatever abnormality he was supposed to see. The examiner sat patiently sucking a biscuit and sipping at a glass of sherry, "Is it normal, would you say?"

"No sir, it's not."

"What's the matter with it then?"

Gabriel peered through the eyepiece hoping for some clue, some inspiration. He decided to chance saying that the appearances suggested tuberculosis. He was going to ask if it could be tuberculosis, but he remembered some advice he had had from a tutor who had told him that an answer to which a commitment is made should not be put in the form of a question because this betrays doubt. "If you decide on an answer," he advised, "you should give it clearly and with conviction. If you are right it impresses the examiners who believe that you know what you are talking about. If you are wrong, it makes no difference. If you answer by putting your statement in the form of a question, the examiners know at once that you have doubts and may even be guessing, and they will put more questions, thus demonstrating to all the extent of your ignorance."

Gabriel hesitated no longer. "It's tuberculosis," he declared.

The examiner shoved the remainder of the biscuit into his mouth, took a sip of sherry, raised an eyebrow and said, "Good man. You're the only one of the lot so far who has managed to see it. That'll do."

"Thank you sir," said Gabriel as he left.

Two days later the results were out, he had passed, and had obtained the highest mark of any student in the orals. One down, two to go, he thought, as he walked home to tell of his success.

He could now relax for a month or so; his next test would not be until the summer, when he would take his final in surgery. He considered this to be the most difficult, one which would require several months' steady work, and attendances at as many clinics and ward rounds as he could manage. He entered for the examination in May and went into the last weeks of intensive study.

When he had completed the question paper, he knew he had done well. He answered questions on the detailed investigation of knee injuries, described the common fractures of the elbow, and the causes of obstruction of the oesophagus, detailed the types of gallstones and enumerated the sorts of whitlow and how to treat them.

In the clinical test he had to interrogate and examine two patients, and afterwards waited anxiously to know if he was to go for his oral. He was. The next day he saw his name on the pass list, and promptly repaired to Neary's. On his way home hours later shuffling along Stephen's Green the thought struck him that failing some disaster such as illness he should pass the medicine final, and be a fully-fledged doctor in about four months. Then what was he to do? In the long term, go to Africa but, for a start, a job in England was the plan. He could gain experience there more quickly than in Ireland, and furthermore, would be better placed to organise his African adventure.

Early in December it was all over. He was finished, a survivor: only about half of those who had started with him were there at the end.

Throughout his training Gabriel had kept his parents in the dark with regard to his progress, and just told them whenever he passed an examination. He never informed them in advance that he was due to take one for fear he might fail. He carried his secretiveness too far, for when he qualified they had no idea he was close to the finish until he arrived home to tell them. As he made little of his success, so did they, and the result was that on conferring day, one of the landmarks of his life, he was the only member of his family at the ceremony.

As he left the college for the last time, his diplomas rolled up under his arm, he thought of how, from being a lazy no-good, regularly beaten schoolboy, he had become a trained professional with an assured future. He stood on the front steps for a few moments, looked across the road to Lord Ardilaun perched on his plinth in Stephen's Green and said aloud, "Well strike me pink, I've done it."

He walked through the Green, passed by the large round flower-bed that had once boasted a statue, until it was blown up, of King George II and headed through the gate at the south-east corner and walked up Leeson Street to arrive at his old school. He went through the arched entrance with the words Catholic University School written above it, traversed the passageway to the chapel entrance but instead of going into the chapel turned to his right and stood at the end of the school playground looking towards the redbrick building at the far end. This was his place of so much suffering, so much bitterness and humiliation. "I never gave in," he said in a low voice, "I got the better of you all, and I've got this to prove it," and he held high his diplomas and his head too, as he turned away to go home.

Chapter 4

Within a few weeks Gabriel had a job in a small seaside town in Essex. When it came to leaving his parents the parting caused him not a tinge of regret. He was glad to be getting away: he had a driving urge to go. It never occurred to him to consider how they felt to have a son they had nurtured and loved, guarded and protected for all his life and, of whom they were very proud, leave them with just a handshake, a kiss and a hug.

One of his brothers drove Gabriel to the North Wall to embark on the *MV Munster* for Liverpool. With his baggage stowed away he held out his hand and said, "Cheerio then, look after yourself."

"Good-bye, old son, God bless you."

Gabriel went to have his supper and shared a table in the saloon with an elderly man. They ignored each other for a time and then the man said, "Excuse me, but are you a doctor?"

"I am," answered the surprised Gabriel.

"I thought you might be."

How does he know? Gabriel pondered. He was wearing no distinguishing marks, no college or hospital tie. He kept quiet, not really wanting to become involved in a conversation. He was acting on his mother's advice when she had warned him that all ships had two menaces on board: gamblers and bores.

"We get many of your sort on these ships," the man went on after an interval.

"Is that so?" murmured Gabriel, a trifle coldly.

"Oh Lord yes, I can pick out you lot a mile off. I travel all the time on this route, and there's always a young doctor on board."

"Is that so?" said Gabriel again.

"Do you know Dr Quinlan?"

"No, I'm afraid not."

"Oh he's a very nice man, a lovely man; you'd like him. He looked after my father for years. He comes from Sligo. Do you know Sligo at all?"

"No I do not."

Gabriel had decided by now that he had met on his very first voyage one of the menaces his mother had so often described. This man was the ship's bore and he must extricate himself from his company at once or suffer him all the way to London. He settled his bill, excused himself and left the table. As he walked away the man asked, as if Gabriel were still there, "Do you know Dr Shaw in Dunratty by any chance?"

When Gabriel arrived on deck the ship was moving down river and he saw all the places he knew so well passing by: the Dodder mouth, the Pigeon House, the causeway with the red bulk of the Poolbeg lighthouse at its end. Here he was at last looking back at the receding lights of Dublin. Only now did he begin to have second thoughts; no longer was his dream a distant desire; he was on his way. He was twenty-four years old, he had £50 and what he stood up in. His qualification gave him a cast-iron meal ticket but nevertheless his feelings were no different from those of all the emigrants before him, despite the fact that he was going because he wanted to, not because he had to.

The next morning he was in Liverpool and in the train for London. Having been brought up on tales of the drabness of England and its destruction by the industrial revolution and the war, he was pleasantly surprised to see what a beautiful landscape there was to enjoy and his preconceived ideas of what to expect were shown to be false.

He stayed a night in London and then took a train for the last lap of his journey. This lasted two hours and he wished it could go on longer, such was his apprehension at the prospect of what lay before him, but eventually his taxi drove up to a building situated in pleasant surroundings with evergreen trees forming a boundary to its grounds, and with the sea in sight a short walk away.

Gabriel staggered into the hallway carrying his baggage to find a woman manipulating plugs in a telephone switchboard. When she saw Gabriel she took off her headphones, beamed on him and said, "Good morning. You must be our new doctor."

"Yes I am. Good morning."

"Welcome then. I'm Mrs Harris. Just one moment and I'll call Jim to help you, and show you your rooms."

She asked him if he had had a good trip, and if this was his first visit to England, and what did he think of it? She told him what a lovely Irish accent he had, and that she was sure he would be very happy with them but awfully busy.

"How many other doctors have you?" inquired Gabriel.

"Just the one."

"That's not too bad. We'll be able to help each other."

"Oh no, there's just the one: you."

Gabriel's heart sank. Who would he ask for advice from minute to minute? What would he do for assistance? How could he look after this place all on his own? He was in a near panic, "But there must be someone else?"

"No," repeated Mrs Harris, "you're the only one resident. The local GPs visit regularly to see their patients but you look after them all the rest of the time."

"But what about the surgery?" asked Gabriel.

"Consultants come periodically and two of the GPs do the emergencies and some of the cold work as well. You'll be assisting them all."

Just as Gabriel was regretting having come, Jim the porter arrived. He was wearing a brown overall jacket, and seemed extremely mournful. He greeted Gabriel lugubriously and lifted one of the suitcases. Then he said, "Now Doctor, if you'll be good enough to take the other bags we can carry your trunk between us and we shall proceed to your rooms."

They walked towards the lift. "It's only one floor," Jim said, "but it facilitates our progress."

As time passed Gabriel was to get used to Jim's quaint way of speaking but for the moment it helped to take his mind from his worries. He had a bedroom and separate sitting-room situated close to the wards, and a bathroom.

"I'm afraid you have to share the bathroom with Matron, Doctor," Jim told him, "but you are unlikely to bump into her unless you are very careless."

When Jim had left, Gabriel started to unpack and wondered where and when he would get his lunch. He did not have long to wait: a maid arrived carrying a tray, "Do you want pale or brown ale?" she asked.

"Pale please," smiled Gabriel.

"Good, I'll bring you some this evening with your dinner. We didn't know which one you'd like."

As he sat down to eat, Gabriel began to think things would not be so bad after all.

"What size white coat do you take?" the maid next asked.

"Forty, I think."

"I'll bring up a few for you when I come to collect the tray."

When she returned with the white coats she told Gabriel that the matron was coming to see him in a few minutes. He had a vision of the traditional hospital dragon, but was pleasantly surprised when he met her. She was quite young, in her mid-thirties. After introducing herself she told him that the hospital had had no resident doctor for over three months and that they had been findings things very difficult, "We have to keep ringing up the GPs all the time," she told him, "and as they have their own surgeries and house-calls to look after, it is often difficult to contact them."

She took him on a tour of the hospital. There was a female ward on the ground floor, and a male ward with a few private rooms above it. There was also a small children's ward. The casualty department and the X-ray room were in a side wing, and in the grounds beside the boiler house was a small mortuary with a post-mortem room behind it.

The next morning they did a ward round together, and at the end she said, "Well Doctor, you're on your own now."

Indeed he was, alone and inexperienced with no immediate colleague to consult. He wondered what the patients would think if they knew how green he really was.

He started each day with a ward round. Then he appeared in the casualty department to see anyone requiring attention, to arrange admissions for patients for operations, to interview and examine new patients and write up their notes for the visiting doctors.

Operations were done on two afternoons a week, and on the other days he continued his general supervision and ward activities, and even found a fair amount of time for reading. He had no official half-day, and was expected to be available at all times. This was not as bad as it sounded, for one or other of the GPs was willing to cover for him if he wanted to go to the cinema. The arrangement enabled him to go to London for day-trips.

Gabriel quickly entered into the routine and became part of the organisation. He had little or no trouble until the day for the first visit of the gynaecologist. This man was scheduled to perform only one operation—a minor one. About an hour before starting time the theatre sister announced that the anaesthetist was unwell and there was no one else available. The surgeon, quite unmoved by this news, looked at Gabriel and said, "You can do it, I can manage my end myself."

Gabriel was horrified, "I've never given a general."

"Oh you'll be all right, she'll be a good one to start on. Just keep her asleep and alive for ten minutes or so, and everything'll be OK."

Gabriel had often watched anaesthetics being given, and was familiar with the machine but he did not feel confident and said so.

"Well don't use it then but keep it handy in case we need to give her oxygen. Start her off on thiopentone and carry on with open ether."

Gabriel rehearsed the exercise very carefully, inspecting the machine to make sure the oxygen cylinder was full.

When the patient was brought to the theatre she was drowsy. Jim and Gabriel transferred her from the trolley to the table, and a short while after her intravenous injection she was deeply asleep. At once the sister prepared her by fixing her legs into stirrups attached to the table to hold them in the correct position. As this was being done, Gabriel moved from his place at the patient's side to sit near her head to hold up her chin as he placed a metal-framed gauze mask over her mouth and nose; holding this in place, he dropped ether from a bottle on it. The surgeon entered and sat himself between the patient's raised legs. "All right to start?" he enquired of Gabriel.

"Yes, go ahead."

"This'll take only a few minutes, Doc. Don't get her too deep."

He worked silently for some time before raising his head over the protecting towels, and looking at Gabriel asked, "Everything OK?"

"Yes I'm fine Doctor," said the patient before Gabriel could answer. He decided then and there that his future did not lie in anaesthetics.

One of Jim's multiplicity of functions was to help nurses to prepare a body for removal from a ward to the mortuary. On the occasion of the first death since Gabriel's arrival Jim came to tell him he would finish the body he was working on following the post-mortem. Gabriel agreed, but he did not realise the significance of Jim's words until the next morning when he came to his room as he was eating breakfast.

"The cadaver is ready, Doctor," he announced in sepulchral tones.

"What cadaver? Ready for what?"

"The man who deceased yesterday Doctor. The cadaver is ready for the post-mortem."

"Oh good. What time is the pathologist coming?"

"There's no pathologist, Doctor, you're doing it."

"But," Gabriel began to protest his ignorance (he had never done a post-mortem on his own) but stopped, not wanting to admit this to Jim, "but I didn't ask for a PM. I know what he died of."

"Even so, Doctor," Jim answered, "we always request of relatives their consent for the procedure in the interests of medical science."

"Well, if you're so bloody interested, you do it!" retorted Gabriel with some heat. "If I need a PM I'll ask for permission myself."

Jim was a bit put out by this outburst, and said he would tell the undertakers to collect the body.

"No," Gabriel ordered. "If you've told everyone we want to do it, I'd better get on with it."

A pathologist can do a simple post-mortem in less than an hour, but it took Gabriel two to decide that he knew the cause of his patient's death was as he had suspected. He felt vindicated. "There, I told you so," he said to Jim, "We've wasted two hours frigging around here, and we're none the wiser. We have added nothing to what we already knew."

"Maybe so, Doctor, but we are safe in the thought that we have explored every avenue."

"So what? I have better things to do than satisfy your morbid curiosity."

Things were never the same between them again but Gabriel thought of what he would have said had the post-mortem revealed an unsuspected cause of death. He now had notions of becoming a pathologist.

Gabriel was taking it easy on a Saturday afternoon when the duty sister called him to a patient who had been operated on a few days previously. The man was complaining of pain at his operation site. Gabriel undid the wide binder-bandage covering his wound and lifted the layers of gauze. As he did, several feet of small intestine spilled out. The stitches had given way and the incision was gaping wide. He replaced the pad before the patient could see anything.

"Ah, that's better, Doc," said the man. "It must have been a bit too tight."

"Yes it was a bit, but we'll have to take you back to theatre to fix things up. Some of the stitches need to be adjusted."

Gabriel went to telephone the surgeon, but he was playing golf and could not be contacted soon enough. He then called the anaesthetist, who thought the whole affair a great joke, and did not stop laughing until Gabriel insisted he come while he repaired the wound.

"For Christ's sake," he yelled into the telephone, "the poor sod's guts are all over the bed. You'll have to come in. He may start bleeding any minute, and he's bound to become infected."

"All right, all right. I'll be there in an hour. Tell sister to get the theatre ready."

It was a relatively simple matter to return the intestine to the abdominal cavity, gently washing it in warm saline and feeding it through the opening, but before Gabriel could get enough stitches in, the patient took a deep, sighing breath, and forced the whole lot out again, but this time the gut cascaded over the side of the table to be held there by the pressure of Gabriel's knee.

"Oh shit, Sister," Gabriel barked, "couldn't you grab the bloody thing for a second?"

Sister, not used to being spoken to in this fashion, threw down the swab she was holding and flounced out of the theatre.

"Now you've done it!" said the anaesthetist, "Florence Nightingale would not have been amused either."

"I'll manage without her," Gabriel said, as he hauled up the man's gut and poured more saline over it before pushing it back where it belonged. This time he took more care to hold it as he stitched.

"There, all done," he announced as the last stitch was tied. "If this guy doesn't get peritonitis, he should live forever."

At this point the sister returned to help put the man back on the trolley. "You shouldn't swear like that," she complained.

"That wasn't swearing, Sister. This is swearing: why the bloody hell...," but he got no further before a hot wet towel hit him in the mouth.

When the surgeon was told of the event he said to Gabriel, "Why all the fuss? Think how useful the experience will be when you're in Darkest Africa."

Going to Africa was Gabriel's long-term dream but to inspect the place, so to speak, before committing himself to a career there, he wanted to become a ship's doctor, and with this in view he went to see the medical superintendent of a shipping line in London, who, when he interviewed Gabriel, said "I suppose you've wanted to do this for years?"

Gabriel said he had, adding that going to sea was the best way he could see Africa and be paid for doing it.

"Oh indeed? Don't get it into your head that you'll see much of Africa this way. One seaport is much the same as another and the job is not an easy one. Don't believe all the rubbish you read of the romance of the sea. Being a ship's doctor is a highly responsible position and hundreds of people will regard you in a special way. You'll be at their beck and call every minute and there'll be no escape from them. They'll consult on trivialities that would be laughed out of any surgery ashore, and remember that they'll be waiting for you to come a cropper, to make a fool of yourself or to fall down drunk some day. Because you'll be the only one in the ship with the power of special knowledge you may not be liked too much and you may thus make some people feel uncomfortable: they'll put you to the test. You'll have only two consolations: one, that no matter how much any of them thinks he knows about medicine, you'll know more, and two, there'll be no coroner."

"I'm used to working on my own," Gabriel told him, showing no reaction to the latter quip. "My present job is a single-handed one."

"Good. Now take off your things, and let me give you the once over."

With the rapid medical examination completed the doctor asked Gabriel when he would be free to join a ship.

"In about three months."

"Right," said the doctor, "you'll have plenty of time to get your kit together. There's a naval outfitters around the corner from here, they'll know what you'll need. Of course, you'll have to pay for all the stuff yourself."

Gabriel nodded.

"Now there's something else," the doctor went on, "do you know anything about dentistry? Have you had any experience in general practice?"

"No, neither."

"Well if I were you I'd try to get a dentist to give me a few tips on dental first-aid, and perhaps the basic technique of pulling a tooth, and I'd ask a GP to take me around with him for a week or two, so that you'll have some idea of what you're likely to come across, particularly with children.

"I can do all that. I know just the people in Dublin."

"Right, that's everything for now then. We'd love to have you. Give me a ring when you're ready, and as soon as a ship is available you can join her."

They shook hands, and Gabriel left to visit the tailor. He had no idea what kit he would need, and put himself in the hands of the outfitter.

"What company will you be joining?" a man with a tape measure around his neck asked him, and when Gabriel told him, said, "Oh that'll cost you, Doctor. You'll be sailing for the tropics and you'll need extra gear."

"Can't be helped" said Gabriel, man of the world, "but I understand we don't have to dress for dinner, so that'll save a few quid."

"That's right Doctor. Things aren't what they used to be. A white high-necked cotton tunic and matching trousers are all you'll need for evening wear in the tropics. Number Tens we call them."

"Good," said Gabriel.

"I'll show you some materials first, Doctor, and when you've chosen the quality of the cloth I'll take your measurements. Will you require an overcoat?"

"I don't think so; just a gaberdine showerproof will do."

When the measuring was finished the tailor said, "We'll dress you from top to toe, and then you'll be off to foreign parts. One last question: will you be serving in a ship as the only doctor, or will there be another?"

"I understand I'll be the only one. What difference does it make?"

"If you are to be the only one, we'll have to give you three gold rings on the cuffs and epaulettes but if there's a senior doctor you will have fewer rings."

Gabriel felt quite superior. There was no harm in starting at the top.

By the time he left the shop he had ordered a shiny peaked cap with company badge and three changeable white cap covers, a navy-blue reefer jacket with golden buttons and three half-inch gold braid bands on each cuff—the braid separated by two quarter-inch bands of red material to show his professional function, navy-blue trousers to match the jacket, three pairs of black socks, various pieces of white cotton underwear, three white shirts with detachable collars and three spares, three white cotton tunics with matching trousers, a pair of epaulettes for the shirts and tunics, three white cotton open-neck, short-sleeved shirts with matching shorts, three pairs of long white stockings, and a pair of white buckskin shoes without toecaps.

"The lot will cost you over £100, Doctor," the tailor said as he totted up the account.

This was the largest sum of money Gabriel had ever spent at one time and on the return journey to the hospital he wondered how long it would take him to pay it.

***

Gabriel was constantly faced with the problem of finding a bed for an emergency admission, and was not surprised when he was asked to accept a patient with pneumonia late one evening. "She's in a bad way, Doc," the GP requesting admission told him, "She lives alone, and just must be in hospital."

"All right," Gabriel agreed, "just give me an hour to see what I can do for her. We're full up."

"I'll order the ambulance now," the doctor told him, "and you should be ready by the time she turns up. She's rather old, and a bit confused."

Forty minutes later, the casualty sister called Gabriel.

"What's up?" he asked.

"There's an ambulance here with a raving maniac in it and the driver says you're admitting her. Is that right?"

"No, I'm expecting a patient, an elderly woman with pneumonia."

"Well she may have pneumonia, but she's trying to break up the ambulance."

When Gabriel reached the front door a few minutes later he could hear the rumpus in the ambulance. "That can't be the patient I'm expecting," he said to the ambulance man.

"Well Sir, she's the patient Dr Limpit ordered us to collect for admission this evening. He said she

99

has pneumonia but half-way here she became violent."

"I'd better take a look at her," Gabriel said as he opened the door of the ambulance.

The inside was a shambles. There were blankets, sheets and dressings all over the place, the second ambulance man was standing with his back to the door with hands held up to protect his head from the missiles being thrown by the patient. "Now Missus," he was saying, "just calm down, the doctor's here to see you."

When the woman saw Gabriel she dropped the pillow she was about to fling, and peered at him. "What sort of doctor are you?" she demanded.

"Just an ordinary one."

"Is that so? You're not one of that lot?" she asked, pointing vaguely to some other place.

"No, I work here in this hospital only. What's all the fuss about?"

"It's that damn doctor of mine. He told me I had pneumonia, and I haven't."

"Well what *is* the matter with you then?"

"Metaphysics," she said, "too much metaphysics. It's all a matter of metaphysics."

"Maybe so, but why break up the ambulance?"

"How can I break up the ambulance when it isn't here, none of us is here? Tell me that now. How?"

"OK. You just sit here quietly and I'll ring Dr Limpit and ask him. We'll see what he has to say for himself."

Gabriel went to the telephone: "She got there all right then?" Dr Limpet asked.

"What the hell is it all about?" Gabriel asked, and went on, "She hasn't got pneumonia. She should be in a nut-house."

"Oh I know that but if I'd told you you wouldn't have accepted her. Just dope her up, and we'll have her certified in the morning. She's been kicking up hell all day, and I can't deal with her now, I'm playing bridge."

"Playing bridge!" Gabriel was about to explode himself when the sister came to tell him that the patient had left the ambulance, which had been promptly driven away, and was now in the hospital asking to be shown to her room.

Gabriel hung-up the telephone and went back to the front hall to find the patient sitting quietly searching through her handbag. She was clad only in her nightdress and dressing gown, with fluffy pink slippers on her feet.

"Now, Missus, I must find out something about you," Gabriel said, sitting down beside her.

"You don't address me like that if you please," his patient said. "I have a name."

"I'm sorry, I don't know your name. Dr Limpit did not mention it when we spoke."

"I'm Alice West. Mrs Alice West. I once had a man who loved me. Children too. All gone. All gone."

Gabriel remained quiet, waiting for her to continue.

"You can't call me Alice. I'm Mrs West. Just because I find myself in this sorry state does not mean that I must lose any more of myself. Why should I be Alice to a stranger? I'm not a child but doctors and nurses seem to think that when one is old and alone they can dispense with formality. I had position, stature. Everything that can be lost only at great cost. You cannot charge me any more than I have already paid. I'm Mrs West. Now, please be good enough to show me to my room. We can talk in the morning."

"I'm afraid we haven't a room; you will have to stay in the ward."

"Show me. I'll decide about that when I see it."

Gabriel led her to the ward and showed her the bed prepared for her. She looked at it, got in, drew the blankets up and said, "I don't like it here. If the colonel knew about this he'd be furious."

Not wanting a further outburst, Gabriel said, "I'm giving you an injection now and I'll move you later when you settle down."

Mrs West said nothing and when she became drowsy Gabriel and the ward sister wheeled her bed into the lift, "This is a private room. I hope it'll be OK, it's just become vacant," he said as he moved away.

Mrs West started to speak, but was overcome by the drug, and fell asleep.

Early next morning Gabriel was called, and arrived to find his patient sitting on the floor rattling the lift gate and screaming in an incoherent way. She resisted all entreaties to calm down, and could only be prevented from harming herself by the quick injection of a further sedative which Gabriel managed to get into her thigh by being quicker than she was.

As she began to submit to the drug, she took Gabriel's hand, "Just an ordinary doctor, are you? To me you're a crafty bastard as well. This is not a private room, it's the bloody lift. I won't forget you, and when I'm dead I'll come back to haunt you, to stand at the foot of your bed with all the other poor souls. You lot all have ghosts around you, the ones you've deceived and killed. They're all around you, they follow you everywhere."

She shut her eyes and let his hand drop. "Don't forget me," she whispered.

***

On his last night in the hospital Gabriel was in bed when he heard a knock on the door. "Come in," he called. It was one of the nurses. "Yes Nurse, what's the matter? I thought you were off duty tonight."

"I am. I've come to say goodbye because I shan't be here in the morning."

"That's very thoughtful of you," said Gabriel, sitting up.

She sat on the edge of the bed facing him, "Well, aren't you going to say goodbye then?"

"Oh yes, goodbye. I hope we'll meet again some time," holding out his hand.

"Oh you *are* slow," she said, leaning forward to kiss him on the cheek.

Gabriel's surprise had turned to shock. All this would have embarrassed him at any time but under these circumstances he was speechless; he did not know what to do. Here he was with a girl offering herself to him, and, paralysed by fears of sin and damnation, he was trying to work out how he could get rid of her without actually ejecting her from his room. She solved the problem. She held his head tightly between her hands and kissed him on the mouth. Then she got off the bed and knelt beside it, leaned forward on her folded arms and said through pouting lips, "Lie down."

Gabriel did as she said, and turned towards her.

"You need a little training, my boy. When a girl comes in your room at night to kiss you goodbye you should respond."

She kissed him again, longer this time, with open mouth. Gabriel kissed her.

"That's better," she smiled.

She began to stroke his hair, and then slipped a hand under the bedclothes and pushed it forward until it lay on him. Then she moved it downwards.

"You shouldn't do that," he murmured.

"Why not?"

"You just shouldn't. It's wrong."

What he wanted to say was that this was a mortal sin, but he reasoned that as she was a Protestant (what else could she be?) there was no point in telling her this; she wouldn't understand, and anyway she might laugh at him.

Her moving hand went lower and played with him. She took her other hand from his head and unbuttoned her blouse which opened all the way down, and then slipping into the bed beside him, whispered, "Don't be a silly boy. I've wanted this for months."

She kissed him again. He was lost. He needed no further prompting. He allowed her to take off his pyjamas, and as he rolled over her, he could hold back no longer.

"That was too quick, Gabriel lad," she pouted. "Lie still for a while and we'll go again."

Much later, when she was leaving, she stroked his cheek in a farewell gesture, "Goodbye my Angel Gabriel. I know I've been the first. There'll never be another like me; there'll never be one the same. You'll never forget me."

In the morning Gabriel left by train for Dublin and on the way he could think of nothing else but his escapade of the night before. He was at once worried about mortal sins and delighted with events, and anyone could have wondered why the young man in the corner seat was smiling to himself from time to time. He analysed the affair in detail and concluded that the moralists were making a great fuss over very little. It's all a load of old rubbish, he told himself, and from that point on he felt better and sex took on a new dimension.

***

When Gabriel was back in Dublin he made arrangements with a dentist friend to spend some time with him to learn the rudiments of dental first-aid. His friend went once a week to a mental hospital, and invited Gabriel to join him there.

At the hospital Gabriel was struck by the apparent normality of everyone he met—or nearly everyone. The patients seemed glad to see him, and chatted about his plans to go to sea. They were quite pleased to play a part in training him. He had been there on several occasions and was in the process of examining a patient when he heard a wolf whistle repeated several times and getting closer.

"Here she comes," said the dentist.

"Who?"

"You'll see. Just say 'good morning' and behave as if there was nothing odd."

At last the place was to live up to Gabriel's expectations, for a few seconds later, the door opened to reveal a tall woman wearing a starched white overall. She was middle-aged and had an untidy mass of grey hair sticking out in all directions like the fronds of a palm tree. Perched on top of her head and held in position with a hairpin, she had a small pointed white nurse's cap. She can't have been whistling, thought Gabriel.

"Good morning, all," she said.

"Good morning, Matron," replied the dentist.

"Good morning," echoed Gabriel, avoiding using the word matron, because he did not really believe it was she. Just then the whistle sounded again. It was coming from behind her, and looking down Gabriel saw that she was being followed by a parrot, which when not whistling, was mumbling and gurgling to itself, and muttering in a hoarse whisper, "Balls, balls."

The matron, for it really was she, noticed Gabriel's look of amazement, and on being introduced by the dentist said, "Don't look so surprised, Doctor. Bongo's all right; he doesn't bite and he's no more ridiculous than a dog."

As she said this she pushed the bird over with her foot. He lay on his side for a few moments, fluttered to his feet, beat bedraggled wings, and said with his head on one side, "Balls, balls. Where have you put the body?"

She looked lovingly at him and said, "Well, I'll leave you gentlemen to get on with the good work. Come along Bongo."

"We all have our idiosyncrasies," said the dentist as the parrot followed her out of the room.

With a fair working knowledge of dental first-aid, Gabriel next joined a general practice. He sat in on surgeries and went on house calls with one of the other doctors. After a few weeks of this he was allowed to make house calls by himself. He went to see a child in Rathgar Road. As he parked outside the house he noticed a dog sitting on the doorstep. He had heard the old stories of postmen being attacked by the family pet so he set off up the garden path with his bag held in front of him to ward off an assault. He climbed up the several steps towards the hall door. The dog showed no sign of malign intent; on the contrary, it stood up wagging its tail in welcome. Gabriel rang the doorbell and waited. When the child's mother opened the door the dog ran into the hall ahead of Gabriel. "Good morning, Mrs Hughes. I'm Dr Gabbett."

"Good morning Doctor. Please come in. Pat's in the front room."

She led him to the sitting-room where the patient, a five-year-old boy, was lying on the sofa. The dog settled itself in front of the fire.

"Good morning Pat," said Gabriel, "I hear you haven't been too well."

He sat on the edge of the sofa and chatted about nothing in particular to gain the child's confidence. Eventually he said, "What's the matter then?"

"I hurt."

"Where?"

The boy pointed vaguely to his chest.

"May I have a look at it?" Gabriel asked while taking a stethoscope from his bag. "And I'd like to listen in with this thing."

Pat said nothing. He was more interested in the dog. Gabriel got down on one knee beside the sofa, and as he did so, the dog walked over and sat down beside him. It placed its chin on his thigh and gazed up at him, wagging its tail.

"I think it might be a good idea to put the dog out in the hall for a while," he said.

"Why?" asked the mother.

"Well he might try to jump up on the sofa while I'm listening into Pat's chest," Gabriel answered, slightly surprised at the question.

"Yes, but why should *I* put him out?" queried Mrs Hughes rather icily.

"Well it can't be my job to do it. He's your dog after all."

"No he's not. He came in with you, I thought he was yours."

"No. He got in when you opened the door to me. He was sitting on the top step when I arrived, and walked in as if he owned the place when you let me in. Whose is he anyway?"

"I don't know. I've never seen him before in my life."

"Well he's a right chancer," said Gabriel. "Leave him where he is, and I'll take him out when I go."

A few days later, on his next house call, the door was opened to him by the patient's wife who said nothing in greeting, but led him to the back of the stairs and indicated the stone steps leading down to the cellar.

"You don't keep the poor man down there, do you?" Gabriel asked.

"Keep who?"

"Your husband, Mr Brennan."

"Oh, do you want to see him?"

"He wants to see me. Dr Gabbett."

"Ohhh," with sudden lightening of manner, "you're the doctor. I thought you were the gasman to read the meter."

Both these incidents, Gabriel felt, tended to diminsh his dignity, and he was quite pleased to know that he was only a temporary G P.

Chapter 5

When Gabriel reported to his ship in the Royal Albert Dock in London he was received on board by an Indian seaman who did not speak English. So he introduced himself by pointing his thumb at his chest and saying "Doctor."

"Doctor Sahib," the man beamed as he helped with the baggage and led him to a cabin with Doctor written on the door. A few minutes later a young officer appeared who said he was Sam, the third officer. "Just leave your things for the present Doc and come and have some tea. You're just in time."

He took Gabriel to the saloon where some of the other officers were already seated around a dining table. They soon discovered that Gabriel had not been to sea before but assured him he had nothing to worry about, that doctoring was much the same wherever it was done.

"You'll be a glorified passenger most of the time Doc," the purser told him, "so make the most of it."

Gabriel was not sure he agreed. He was already feeling the responsibility the venture would place on him but he was not prepared to argue the point at this time.

When tea was finished Sam said to Gabriel, "I'm off at eight, Doc. If you like we'll go ashore for a drink."

Gabriel went back to his cabin to finish his unpacking. A steward appeared. "Doctor Sahib?" he enquired.

"Yes, that's me."

"I'm looking after you, " the man said, "I'm Shorty."

He was at least six feet two tall.

"What's your proper name?"

"Fernandes."

"Well, I'll call you Fernandes, then."

"No good, Sahib. The ship has a Goan crew in the saloon and there are seven or eight called Fernandes. Everyone knows me as Shorty."

"All right. Shorty it is then, if that's what you want."

"You ready for bath now?" Shorty asked.

"Later," Gabriel answered, a little surprised at the question.

"Ready now," Shorty went on, as he took a towel and a bar of soap, "ready now. I am putting these in the bathroom; you come now."

Gabriel did not normally have a bath so early in the evening but rather than explain this said, "All right, you go on. I'll be there in a minute."

He undressed and put on a bathrobe, and found the steward outside his door waiting to show him the way to the bathroom. He ushered him in and gave him the towel and soap before leaving. The bath was a large metal Victorian type and a board was placed across it on which was a smaller enamel bath containing hot water. Gabriel discovered that the normal bath taps gave only sea water, and it had been the steward's job to fill the smaller bath with fresh. There were also some enamel jugs with cold fresh water in them.

Gabriel soaked in the bath thinking, Christ, this is the life of Riley. What would they say at home if they could see me now, with a fellow to fill the bath for me, and even to carry the soap and towel? Christ Almighty!

So the first day was turning out to be very satisfactory. He had a pleasant and commodious cabin with a steward to look after him who not only drew his bath but took care of his laundry. He also laid out clean clothing every day and even changed cufflinks and epaulettes. He brought meals to the cabin if Gabriel did not want to go to the saloon, making sure he supplied the best cuts of meat in lavish quantity.

Despite Shorty's apparent knowledge of English his ability was limited to basic words and phrases required for his job, and this prevented Gabriel getting to know much about him. In order to try to correct this Gabriel bought a book devoted to teaching English-speaking sailors the rudiments of Hindustani. Unfortunately, it was primarily intended for deck and engineer officers and contained relatively little of use to the doctor but he learned the numbers and the names of a few illnesses which he found quite useful in his daily surgeries. The book would have been a godsend if he had wanted the wick in the compass light trimmed or wished to tell someone a man had fallen off a derrick into the water.

On his way back to the ship on his first night after being to a pub in North Woolwich with Sam, Gabriel bought some pork pies and asked him if they had any way of heating them back in the ship. "Sure I'll heat them for you, Doc," said Sam.

When they were back on board he led Gabriel to the surgery, where he emptied the water from the small sterilizer used for the medical instruments and syringes, switched it on, put the pork pies in it and exclaimed, "Two piping hot pork pies coming up. They'll take a few minutes, Doc. I'll see if I have any beer topside. I'll be back in a jiffy."

When he returned Gabriel voiced his concern at the misuse of the medical equipment. "Not to worry Doc," Sam assured him, "but mind you don't go washing socks in it. It's our pie heater, and we wouldn't want you messing it up."

At breakfast on Gabriel's second day the purser told him he would take him to meet the captain, "It's usual for the MO to be available for an hour or so every morning in the surgery. So you'd better put on your uniform and be there in case any of the crew wants to see you. I'll come along later and take you up to see the Old Man. After that we'll go to the shipping office and get you signed on; otherwise you won't get paid."

So, dressed up in his spanking new uniform with the three gold stripes on the cuffs, Gabriel went to the surgery, and while waiting for anyone to come spent his time in checking the instruments and drugs supplied for his use.

Gabriel found the captain to be a gruff type with very little to say. "You're a newcomer to this life, I believe, Doc?" he asked.

"Yes, sir."

"Well don't let it bother you. You won't be overworked here."

This brought a laugh from the purser which disappeared instantly when the captain added, "But you won't be the only one."

"How long before we sail?" Gabriel wanted to know.

"In about a week. How long do you intend staying at sea?"

"I have no idea at present."

"No doubt you'll want to stay until you wear out the new suit," the captain said, waving at Gabriel's shiny buttons.

A long silence followed. "Have you signed on yet, Doc?"

"No sir, we're going to the shipping office now."

"Good. Well I shan't keep you any longer. Good morning."

The purser told Gabriel to meet him at the gangway in ten minutes, but when they did, the purser said, "You can't go ashore like that. Why haven't you changed?"

"What do I want to change for? You told me earlier to put this thing on, now you're telling me to take it off again."

"You can't go ashore in uniform. Only fifth engineers do that."

Gabriel went back to change. First lesson in protocol, he thought.

At the shipping office he signed the papers and had his photograph taken for the identity card.

As sailing day approached officers who had been on leave returned to the ship. Stores were taken on and the loading of cargo completed. On sailing day a special train brought the passengers to the dockside and within two hours the ship was going through the locks into the Thames. It was early evening before they were sailing free of tugs down river: Gabriel's great adventure had begun. At last, after all the years of waiting and dreaming, he was on the last leg of his journey to Africa—the first stop: Port Said.

He soon became accustomed to the routine of shipboard life, running morning and evening surgeries and sometimes seeing passengers in their cabins. He was struck by the utter triviality of most of the complaints presented to him. There were nearly three hundred and fifty people on board with one doctor to look after them. Ashore, there would have been at least two thousand, but having a doctor as "part of the family" made people less hesitant to come for advice. He was quite content not to be overworked by major disorders, for he was very limited in his ability to deal with these, not only by lack of experience, but by the absence of any skilled help from X-rays or pathology tests.

The fact that the ship's company seemed to have unbounded confidence in him did not make Gabriel's burden any lighter; in fact it made things worse because it indicated that they would expect him to rise to the occasion as required. After all, they must have reasoned, as they were all highly trained, efficient in their jobs and capable of dealing with any emergency, so was their doctor.

They were off Cape Bon when the chief officer's steward told Gabriel that his Sahib wanted to see him. Gabriel arrived at his cabin to find the chief seated in an armchair with a glass in his hand. "Hello Doc. Come in."

"Hello Bob. What can I do for you?"

"Nothing, old boy. I've been too busy since we left London to have had much of a chance to talk to you but now that we're well on our way and things have settled down, it's time we had a drink. Gin OK?"

"Yes, fine," said Gabriel, sitting down.

"Good," the chief said, as he opened a new bottle of gin and threw the cap into the sea.

"What did you do that for?" Gabriel asked.

"Why not? We don't want bloody bottle caps all over the deck, do we?"

He half-filled two tumblers and handed one to Gabriel. "Cheers Doc," he said, taking a long swig.

"May I have some water or tonic in this?" Gabriel enquired.

"Sure, help yourself," indicating a vacuum flask of iced water on the table.

Gabriel poured as much as he could fit in the glass. "Cheers," he said, and gulped down a drink. Christ, he said to himself, this'll kill me. I hope someone else comes to help finish off the bottle, but no one came and in less than an hour he had finished somewhere in the region of a third of a bottle of gin. He had to get away from this man when he could still move. What would anyone think if they saw their young doctor drunk on the high seas? For many who travelled by sea, it might be what they expected: ships' doctors were all alcoholics in their book.

"I must go, Bob," Gabriel said, climbing to his feet.

"Not at all Doc, sit down. Have another."

"No thanks, I can't. I drink very little and anyway, what shall I do if I'm needed?"

"Never mind that Doc. Tell them you're seasick and if the worst comes to the worst we can bury your mistakes before Port Said."

Far from reassuring Gabriel, this remark brought him to his senses and, quite determined, he put down his glass and staggered off. He reached his cabin by walking aft along the boat deck and climbing down outside ladders to the main deck. He met no one, and was congratulating himself on having reached "home" unobserved when the telephone rang. He picked it up. "Hello Doc," he heard the chief's voice say, "for Christ's sake come up here. I've opened up my hand on one of these bloody glasses."

Gabriel climbed topside again to find the chief sitting on a chair beside the hand basin with his bleeding hand held under a running tap. Blood was streaming out from a gash in the palm. Gabriel wrapped it in a towel and held it tightly. "How did you do it?" he asked.

"I went to put the glass on the shelf but it slipped and I instinctively grabbed at it. But it hit the edge of the basin just as my hand reached it and shattered."

"It's quite a long cut but not too deep. The tendons don't seem to have been cut. I'll have to stitch it for you, though. Hold the towel in place and come down to the surgery."

In the surgery the chief lay on the examination couch while Gabriel went to find someone to help him. He returned with Sam whom he detailed off to hold the tray of instruments he had laid out.

"You won't need a local for this, Bob, " he said, "you've got enough booze in you to deaden anything. I'll do a nice neat job on this for you but you must stay quite still."

He need not have spoken for the chief was now in a deep sleep.

"OK, Sam. Just hold his wrist for me, and I'll try not to stitch you to him. My head is swimming."

Sam did not answer. His eyes were disappearing under their lids and Gabriel held him as he slid to the deck. He placed a pillow under his head and went back to his work with one eye closed to see better. When he was satisfied with the quality of the stitches he dressed the wound. Then, steadying himself with any handrail available, he slowly worked his way back to his own cabin.

The next morning Gabriel was up only just in time to meet the captain at the head of the main stairs at the start of their daily inspection of the ship. It was one of Gabriel's functions to be part of the team and he fell in at the end of the little procession as it moved away.

The round of the ship was nearly complete when the captain said he wanted to have a look at the hospital and, as the door was locked, asked Gabriel for the key.

"I haven't got it, sir."

In fact Gabriel had never even been into the hospital which was beside the surgery. The captain turned to the second officer. "Who's got the key?"

"The chief steward, sir."

"Why hasn't the doctor got it?"

"Because the chief steward needs it to keep the place clean, sir."

"Get it."

Eventually the captain went into the hospital followed by Gabriel and the second officer. There was a locker standing against the far bulkhead separating the two beds; otherwise the room was empty but on the locker was a huge cake covered in white icing. It had a solitary red candle in the centre and the words, "Happy Birthday Fred," beautifully written around the edge in blue icing.

"Is this for your birthday, doctor?" the captain asked unsmilingly.

"It's not mine, sir. I've never been in here before."

"Well you bloody well should have been."

"It's got nothing to do with me. Maybe the chief steward knows something about it."

"I'm damn sure he does. It'll be his fucking cake. From now on you keep the key of this place. I'll deal with the chief."

Gabriel never really found out who was responsible for the cake or how it came to be in the hospital. He never knew what became of it but Sam told him it was a Cargo Brand cake. Anything anyone acquired or made from cargo or ship's stores fell into this category. There was Cargo Brand paint, Cargo Brand whisky, Cargo Brand rope; in fact any commodity could acquire the label. For all Gabriel knew he was sailing in a Cargo Brand ship.

On arrival at Port Said Gabriel was standing on the bridge as the ship approached its mooring, gliding past the de Lesseps statue and opposite to a large department store bearing a neon sign reading Simon Arzt on its façade.

The ship was flying an assortment of flags and Gabriel asked a cadet what they all signified.

"Well, Doc, the one at the foremast is always the flag of the country we're visiting: Egypt. The four-flag hoist on the yardarm is the ship's radio call-sign, and identifies us. The white triangular one with Royal Mail written on it speaks for itself, and the plain yellow one is yours."

"What do you mean, mine?"

"It's the Q-flag. It means 'My ship is healthy, I require free pratique.' It's a signal to the Port Health people that there's no infection on board. No one can leave or come aboard the ship until it is lowered."

"Who does that then?"

"You do. You're supposed to be at the rail to meet the shore doctor and fill out all the forms. If I were you, Doc, I'd get down there; he should be here any minute."

This was all news to Gabriel. Halfway down to the gangway, he met the purser coming up. "Where the hell have you been Doc? The bloody MO is waiting for you."

"How was I supposed to know that? Nobody told me I had to meet anyone."

They went to the ship's office where Gabriel introduced himself to the waiting medical officer. He was studying some forms. "Have you any dead bodies or feathers on board?" he asked.

"Dead bodies or feathers?" queried Gabriel. "Do you mean feather feathers? You know from chickens?"

"Yes I do. Have you any?"

"Well how do I know?"

"You should know. It's your business to know what the ship is carrying."

Gabriel turned to the purser. "Well, have we any feathers?"

"If they're not on the manifest, we haven't any. All the chickens and turkeys in the freezers are pre-plucked."

"We have no feathers, Doctor," Gabriel told the MO.

"Well, sign the papers please."

When this was done the MO told Gabriel he could take down the Q-flag.

"Go back to the bridge and tell the Old Man," the purser said.

Gabriel went back topside. The captain asked, "What was all the delay Doc?" and then, before Gabriel could answer, went on, "Some of these bastards couldn't crap on time."

Gabriel left well alone and prepared to go ashore.

***

They were steaming in the Red Sea heading for Port Sudan. Gabriel was leaning on the rail gazing into the water when the head waiter came to stand beside him. "Hi Doc," he said.

"Hello Barney. How's things?"

"Not so bad. Why aren't you fixed up yet?"

"What do you mean. Fixed up?"

"Oh come off it Doc. You know what Byron had to say about it."

"About what?"

"You know Doc:

What men call gallantry and the gods adultery
Gets more common when the weather's sultry.

For Christ's sake man, the bloody passengers have been at it since we passed Gibraltar."

"How do you know?" asked Gabriel.

"I keep my eyes and ears open. There's not much goes on in this ship that I don't know about. I could show you quite easily who's knocking who and I also know that you're not gettin' it yet."

"Is that so?"

Gabriel felt uneasy at the confidence Barney displayed but before he could say more, Barney went on, "I have a lovely little pancake for you. Just the job. Her name's Barbara, and she's about twenty. She's got her mother with her though."

"A fat lot of use that is," scoffed Gabriel.

"Not at all Doc. All you have to do is to give it to Mum first. She'll be so bloody pleased with herself she won't notice you're screwing the daughter on the side."

"Ah don't be silly Barney. How could I do that?"

"Easy, Doc, if you wanted to, but I'll tell you what I'll do. I'll take the mother off your hands and you watch out for the girl. I rather go for older women: they're always so bloody grateful."

Gabriel laughed at this but felt that Barney was not joking; he really meant what he was saying.

"Well it's time for the surgery, Barney, I must be off."

"Cheers Doc. Now you take a look. Very nice."

* * *

Port Sudan was dry, harsh and hotter than Gabriel had imagined. The stevedores, tall and handsome, moved in unison, making heavy work look easy. Through a glass-bottomed boat he looked on the coral reef and its luxuriance of life and felt if for that alone Port Sudan had been worthwhile.

By now he was so immersed in his new environment that he felt part of it, more closely united to it than he had ever been to the one he had left behind in Ireland. He had no idea why, but he felt more at home looking towards the desert in Port Sudan than he had ever known leaning against the Poolbeg lighthouse looking to the horizon in a dream.

The ship sailed on to Aden, rounded Cape Guardafui and headed for Mombasa. At the end-of-voyage fancy dress ball Gabriel lost no time in dancing with Barbara who had gone as a Folies Bergères girl in black and red tights with matching halter. She agreed to come to his cabin when the dancing was over but when she arrived he was disappointed that she had changed her costume and was now wearing a conventional evening gown which reduced considerably her areas of immediate accessibility.

"Why did you change?" he wanted to know with evident irritation.

"Because Mother said I should before coming down here."

"You didn't tell her you were coming here to see me, did you?"

"Of course I did. She always likes to know where I am. She may come and join us later."

"Ah well, it can't be helped. Would you like something to drink?"

"Orange, please."

"Don't you want anything in it?"

"Yes, just ice and water."

Gabriel's spirits sank as he prepared the drink, "Where are you going in Kenya?" he asked.

"Eldoret. My father has a business there."

The conversation continued in this vein, as she told him of her life in her father's office, and Gabriel was becoming more bored than desperate and felt that all he wanted was to go asleep.

"You'll love the fruit in Kenya," she told him.

"Good."

"Particularly the pineapples. If you boil them with lots of sugar, they're just as good as the tinned ones."

"Drink up," said Gabriel. "I'll take you back to your mother."

***

The passengers left the ship at Mombasa and as most of the cargo was discharged there Gabriel had a week to explore the town and hinterland. He contacted a local doctor and visited clinics. What he saw had a great impact on him and made him more determined to make a career there.

The ship went south to Beira and at each port of call on the way he made similar visits. In this way he began to get a fair grasp of what medical practice meant in the tropics. On the way north again the ship stopped at Zanzibar to take on fresh water. There was another ship of the same company anchored there and the doctor, a retired army medical officer, came to visit Gabriel to ask if he could come to see a man who was causing him some concern. Gabriel agreed and in the launch the doctor told him that the patient had been complaining of vague abdominal pain for several days which was so bad that he could not walk. Yet he had no fever. "I'm at a loss to know what ails him," explained the doctor, "and I felt I should take the opportunity of having a second opinion before deciding whether or not to land the man."

On boarding the other ship Gabriel was led to the hospital but before opening the door the doctor signalled to Gabriel to remain silent and to listen. Gabriel heard nothing and after a few seconds they went inside. As soon as they did, the man lying there began moaning. Gabriel examined him carefully and when he was finished, shook his head and stood up to leave followed by the other doctor. As soon as they were back on deck the other said, "Well, what do you think of him?"

"I don't believe he's seriously ill," Gabriel replied. "He's not feverish and all my tapping and prodding and listening to his chest indicated nothing abnormal."

"Did you find *anything* wrong with him?"

"No," answered Gabriel, "nothing. I found nothing. He is quite a puzzle."

"He's no bloody puzzle to me," was the unexpected response to this statement. "Let's go back in again."

Once inside the hospital again, the doctor lifted the man out of bed by his hair, grabbed the back of his neck and the seat of his pants, and propelled him out on deck. "Get back to work, you bastard," he shouted, kneeing him in the behind and sending him scurrying off to the crew's quarters.

"What did you do that for?" asked the incredulous Gabriel.

"Don't look so shocked, dear boy. I know it's not what you'd see in Harley Street but this isn't bloody London, you know, and I've suspected for days that that sod has been having me on. I just wanted confirmation of my opinion before I dealt with him. Come and have a drink and some lunch."

He headed off for the bar, leading Gabriel by the arm. "Tell me something about this penicillin stuff, dear boy. Is it any good?"

***

When the ship returned to Mombasa to take on cargo and passengers for the return voyage there was also a change of crew, the new one having arrived from Bombay in one of the company's other ships.

The first and most popular stop on the way to England was Aden, a free port where all kinds of goods: cameras, watches and jewellery could be bought at a fraction of United Kingdom prices. On the evening prior to arrival two members of the deck crew reported sick. When Gabriel saw them he found they both had a high fever and a rash. He had never seen smallpox but even one of his limited experience could suspect it as the men had been in India within the previous two weeks. He was not certain of the diagnosis, and there was no other doctor on board to whom he could turn for help. "We must inform the Old Man and get a message to Aden," he told the chief officer.

They found the captain in his dayroom. "Shit," he growled, "where did that come from?"

"They caught it in India," Gabriel told him, "but they have old vaccination marks. They may not be seriously affected themselves but they are a danger to others."

"What are you going to do about it?"

"I'm going to check the rest of the crew and vaccinate them."

"What about the passengers?"

"Well none of them will have had any contact with the deck crew, so it's extremely unlikely that there is a great risk but we can check their vaccination certificates."

"We don't want any panic you know. Could we leave checking them until we get in tomorrow? We'll be there at dawn."

"Yes, I suppose we could but they're all looking forward to going ashore and they'll be bloody annoyed at not being told in advance that they're to be kept on board."

"They'll have to put up with it. I'd sooner stop them at the last minute if we have got smallpox rather than tell them we have it now and then if it turns out that we haven't, tell them they can go after all. It'd make you look bloody silly Doc."

"That's right," said the chief. "If I were you Doc, I'd keep quiet until the port MO has seen these men."

"All right," agreed Gabriel.

So it was decided. Gabriel vaccinated the crew; then did the captain and himself. He had dinner in his cabin to avoid questions from any passenger who might have noticed the increased pace of his professional activities.

The next morning the port MO confirmed Gabriel's diagnosis. "The ship is quarantined," he declared, "nobody comes on board or goes ashore without official control. We'll care for these men in the hospital here. The ship can sail after all the formalities have been completed."

"Right," Gabriel said, and went to tell the captain.

As he made his way to the bridge he had to squeeze past passengers congregated at the head of the gangway. When the captain heard the news he ordered Gabriel to tell the passengers. Gabriel hesitated, "Can't the purser do it? He does all the other announcements."

"Oh no Doc. This is your big moment, you do it. Tell Sparks to organise it for you."

When he was handed the microphone he had no time to consider what to say, and here he was about to tell a hundred and fifty passengers eager to get ashore to buy their "goodies" that the trip was off. He thought of himself momentarily as Tyrone Power or Clark Gable saying, "Now hear this. Now hear this. This is the captain speaking. We have been hit by two torpedoes but we're still afloat, and by thunder we'll get this old bucket to San Diego if it takes the rest of the war to do it." But all he heard around him was an amplified gurgle which he guessed must be coming from him. The radio officer switched off the microphone and said, "For Christ's sake, Doc, just tell them there's smallpox on board; they can't go ashore and they're all going to be vaccinated."

Gabriel started again, "Good morning, ladies and gentlemen, this is the doctor speaking. May I have your attention please? Two members of the deck crew are suffering from smallpox and are being taken ashore. The ship has been placed in quarantine and no one will be allowed to leave or board us in Aden. We shall want to vaccinate everyone as an added precaution even though most of you will probably have been done within the past three years. Thank you."

By lunchtime, all the passengers had been vaccinated, except for four who had refused, and the ship was bound for Suez. On arrival there the port MO interviewed Gabriel and told him that the four passengers would not be allowed to continue their voyage. Gabriel explained that they had a right to refuse vaccination and that anyway they all held valid certificates.

"Maybe so," the MO said, "but the ship cannot go through the Canal with these people on board.

If they won't be done now they must either come ashore and be held in quarantine here or if they remain on board, the ship will not be allowed to proceed."

When the captain was told he barked, "Well they'll bloody well have to be vaccinated or stay in Suez, because we're sailing in a few hours with or without them. Christ, there's always some awkward bastards around. Why can't they be done like everyone else, and not cause all this trouble? Anyone would think they were being castrated."

When Gabriel explained the position to the four there was much abusive talk about jumped-up quacks and officious bureaucrats but they all agreed to submit to the MO's orders. One of the four was very vociferous in his condemnation of all doctors and presented his arm for the needle scratch like a *Boys' Own Paper* hero facing a firing squad but when the needle touched his arm he slumped to the deck and was laid out on the examination couch for the work to be completed.

Gabriel apologised to the MO for the coolness of the reception he had received on board. The doctor thanked him. "It doesn't matter," and added, "It's all very well for people to be difficult in dealing with these matters but if smallpox gets into Europe by way of the Suez Canal, I'm the one who would be held responsible. I don't care if everyone on board had a certificate signed by Winston Churchill; nobody gets past here in a ship which has just had smallpox on board unless he has been vaccinated since the disease appeared."

"I'll pass that on," Gabriel assured him as they bade farewell at the head of the gangway.

The whole affair of the four recalcitrant passengers was blamed on the "desire for the Egyptians to get even for the way King Farouk was treated during the war," a passenger told Gabriel.

By Gibraltar the ship was out of quarantine; there were no further cases. The sight of the Rock regenerated imperial morale, and the prospect of being home for Christmas occupied all thoughts. When they were within a few days of London, signs of homecoming began to appear: mature men became pranksters and went about in boisterous fashion, playing practical jokes and giving every appearance of high good humour. This condition was known as The Channels and was induced by the contemplation of home triggered by the cooling of lavatory seats.

Gabriel stayed aboard for Christmas and went to midnight mass with one of the cadets. On their way in the bus they sat opposite a man who drank from a whiskey bottle and had a dead hare under his arm. He stroked its head and carried on a ventriloquist act. He repeated his lines over and over, laughing louder each time. "Who's coming for Christmas dinner then?"

"Me," he answered himself in a high squeaky voice gazing at the hare.

"Hare today and gone tomorrow," he roared, and took another swig from the bottle.

The cadet told Gabriel he was not a Catholic but liked midnight mass because "the RCs put on a good show, and really make you feel it's Christmas."

In the church they sat in a pew at the back. All went well until a man who had been standing in a side aisle fell to the floor. There was a rush of people to his assistance. He was lifted up and carried to the porch to be propped in a chair. Gabriel felt obliged to help him, and undid his collar and tie. He sensed an overpowering smell of alcohol and noticed the man's bleary eyes; he concluded he was dead drunk. The fall did not seem to have damaged him, and he sat quietly, taking stock of his surroundings. One of the bystanders remarked that there was steam coming from the top of his head: no doubt due to the cold air from the open church door.

"Where's his hat? Put on his hat," someone suggested.

"Not in the church. You can't put on his hat in the house of the Lord," another man declared.

With attention diverted from him, Gabriel took the cadet aside and said, "The sooner we get out of here the better. If you want a Christmas show, you can come back in the morning."

***

Gabriel's next voyage was to Australia and once again he found himself installed in great comfort sailing south and east. He was now far more confident than he had been in his first ship and ready to take anything in his stride.

They were sailing for Brisbane, north-about Australia with two stops on the way: Marseille and Aden.

The captain was enjoying his first command. He was less autocratic than the one on the voyage to East Africa, and did not require his MO to follow him around the ship on his daily inspection; he just required that he be informed of anything which might affect the health of the ship's company.

There were forty cadets on board, and on his first meeting with the cadet officer, Gabriel was asked to give them lectures on the dangers of venereal diseases, particularly as the ship was to spend two or three days in Marseille.

"These chaps'll fuck anything Doc," the officer told Gabriel, "so for God's sake make sure they know what it's all about."

Gabriel was far from sure that he knew himself what "it" was all about but at least, however little knowledge he had, he knew more about the subject than his pupils. Yet that was only partly true. He certainly knew more about venereal diseases than any of them, but his knowledge of "it" was nowhere near as advanced. Most of them had been at least a year or two at sea and all of them had been to Mediterranean ports before.

The first lecture went well, though the questions at the end landed Gabriel with more than he had bargained for. These had little or nothing to do with VD but were concerned more with sexual mechanics. One of the most talkative of the youths was an eighteen-year-old known to all as Fingers. He told them of a knee-trembler he had had in Genoa.

"Oh come off it Fingers," scoffed one of his friends, "you never had it at all."

Then, addressing Gabriel, he added, "Fingers is short for Finger-fucker, Doc, because that's all he ever gets."

Gabriel felt things were getting out of control and told them to be quiet, to confine themselves to questions relating to the subject of the lecture.

"My older brother says that you're not a sailor until you've had a dose seven times," announced another.

"Now stop it," ordered Gabriel, "if you haven't any proper questions, that'll be all for today."

"Have you got a clapometer Doc?" someone wanted to know.

"What's that?"

"It's a gadget you shove up a bloke's tool, and if you put your ear to it you can hear the clap."

The session ended in gales of bawdy laughter. The second one went no better but was nevertheless enjoyed by all. Gabriel was sorry there were not to be more; they were of greater value to him than to the cadets.

***

After the ship left Marseille the captain asked Gabriel, "Did any of the cadets pick up anything in Marseille, Doc?"

"Pick up what?" Gabriel asked purposely uncomprehending.

"Oh you know. Did any of them get any undesirable infections? You know, from the girls there."

Gabriel was not inclined to answer. He wondered what the Old Man would call a desirable infection, but said, "I would regard anything I knew about any of them, learned in my professional capacity, to be privileged."

"Oh no Doctor," becoming more formal, "I am entitled to know everything."

"If I issue a medical certificate ashore, excusing someone from work, I am not required to state the diagnosis."

"Well ships are different, Doctor."

"Maybe so; but I can't answer the question. What do you want to know for anyway?"

"It's not curiosity Doctor. I want to know so that if I should meet one of the chaps who has caught something, I shan't say good morning to him."

Gabriel was speechless, so said nothing. After a prolonged silence the captain said, "Well, if you won't tell me, you won't tell me. So we'll have to agree to differ."

Gabriel was greatly relieved, because to have a row with the captain, particularly at the start of a long voyage could have serious consequences. He stood up. "If there's nothing else I'll be getting below; it's nearly time for my surgery."

"Yes all right Doc."

Gabriel left, and gave some thought to his captain. A decent fellow, he mused. Friendly enough, a bit pompous, but what ship's captain is not? As time went on he got to know the man better and he was struck by the fact that he never finally made up his mind about anything without changing it at least once. Every morning he exhibited this facet of his personality when he ordered his breakfast. His steward customarily stood behind his chair while the Old Man studied the menu. This took a minute or two and eventually he would order, for example, bacon and a fried egg. The steward would then leave to give the order in the galley but before he reached the door of the saloon the captain would shout after him, "Make it a scrambled egg."

If he had ordered a scrambled egg he would change his order to a fried egg or poached egg or even an omelette. He did this every morning and at all other meals. The officers waited to see how far the steward could get before being shouted at. If he got out of earshot before the final decision the Old Man would say to no one in particular, "I thought I'd rather like a boiled (or poached, or fried, or scrambled) egg this morning."

His most spectacular change of mind occurred in the Strait of Messina. Gabriel was leaning on the rail looking at the passing shore when the ship began to turn around, eventually describing a full circle. He was astonished at this manoeuvre, very risky in such narrow waters, and wondered if there was something wrong with the ship's steering gear. He learned later from the chief officer what had happened: the captain had decided that he would not give way to a ferry crossing from the mainland to Sicily, having previously announced that he would, and as he could not stop the ship in time, had had to make a circle. "The old fart," the chief complained, "I'll bet if he goes for a shit, he ends up brushing his teeth."

**

The ship worked its way around the Australian coast and while it was berthed at Fremantle a few days before commencing the voyage home, Gabriel had the opportunity to make an overland trip to Carnarvon, the site of a whaling station from which catchers operated in Shark Bay and the adjoining ocean. He had been invited to spend a day on a whale chaser, a ship resembling a large trawler. It was actually a converted wartime corvette, but there were differences: a harpoon gun on the fo'c'sle and a catwalk leading from the bridge to the gun position.

The mast served as a giant fishing-rod. The line from the harpoon passed back to it whence it led through a series of pulleys to a system of springs in the hold.

The harpoon was a steel rod over four feet long and several inches in diameter. It had a slot running its length in which there was a ring attached to the line, the ring being able to travel the full length of the slot. When the harpoon was loaded into the gun the ring was pushed up close to the barbs but was drawn to the end of the harpoon when the gun was fired. The head had four barbs fitted to the shaft on a swivel and before the harpoon was loaded these barbs were tied tightly into grooves in the sides of the shaft, fixing the head to it and preventing any movement. At the tip of the head there was a charge which went off some seconds after firing. The effect of the explosion was to release the barbs allowing the head to swivel. This reduced the risk of withdrawal, while the shock wave was sufficient to kill the whale if it was hit in the vicinity of a vital organ. Sometimes a second or even a third harpoon had to be discharged to finish the job.

The ship steamed about for some time before whales were sighted. The captain, who was also the harpoonist, left his position on the bridge and went along the catwalk to stand behind the gun. He chose a female first, because in the event of a hit, any bulls who were close would be likely to stay near and he could kill them too. He used hand signals to direct the ship towards the quarry at full speed. He manipulated the gun to make sure it was free and checked the position of the line running from the harpoon.

The whale was about four hundred yards ahead but she sounded as they drew closer. The ship slowed but stayed on course, the harpoonist hoping he would be in a good firing position when the animal resurfaced. A man in the crow's nest shouted "Starboard bow," when he saw the whale coming up again. The gun fired. The harpoon with the line snaking out behind it drove into the animal's back. Gabriel heard the charge explode, and watched the whale sink beneath the water drawing out the line as the mast and springs took the strain. When she reappeared, bloody foam and water spewed from her blowhole. She writhed in the waves, moaning and gasping for breath as she churned the pink-red water. She gave a long, shuddering sigh, rose one great slender flipper in the air and died. The sun was shining very brightly, and Gabriel watched a shark gliding by.

The line was winched in until the carcase was alongside, a pipeline was forced through the skin and blubber and air pumped through it to make the body buoyant. Then it was made fast as the ship gathered speed again.

Gabriel saw four more whales killed. He was saddened by the ease of it all, the waste. No pitting of skill and stamina in an open whaler in freezing weather, no throwing a harpoon in hope of a strike, and then no fear being towed around the ocean by a fighting dangerous beast, no fight to avoid destruction in icy water. There was none of that, it was a leisurely warm-day exercise with oblivious animals coming up under the muzzle of a gun no more than five yards distant.

"How long will you go on killing whales?" Gabriel asked the captain.

"Until they're all gone Doc."

***

On the voyage from Fremantle to Aden, when the ship was as far from land as it was possible to get, a passenger with a violent toothache asked Gabriel for help. He had had the pain for hours and could bear it no longer.

Fortunately, one of the passengers was a doctor, and he agreed to help too. The tooth would have to come out. Gabriel would give the anaesthetic while the other doctor pulled the tooth. The patient was put lying on one of the hospital beds. Gabriel injected the anaesthetic, and the "dentist" got to work. It was a difficult extraction and it was necessary to put a stitch in the man's gum; so while Gabriel stayed with the patient the other went to the surgery to get a needle and some silk for the suture. He was unable to find them and called to Gabriel for help. When he had got what they required they returned to the hospital but there was no patient. "Christ he's gone," gasped Gabriel, "he can't have got far. You look for'ard, I'll go aft."

Gabriel found his patient. He was leaning over the poopdeck rail watching the ship's wake, about to fall into the sea. Gabriel said nothing. He just lunged at the man and grabbed him by the waist.

"Bloody good Doc," slurred the patient, "bloody good, I didn't feel a thing, it's better already. Bloody good, let's have a drink."

Gabriel guided him back to the hospital where he fell asleep as soon he was put on a bed. The other doctor returned. "Christ Almighty,"spluttered Gabriel, "he was on the afterdeck rail. Another second and he'd have been over the wall. I need a stiff drink. What'll you have?"

In the morning the patient felt fine except for a mild ache in his jaw. He had no recollection of his escapade. Gabriel said nothing; if something's working, he thought, why fix it?

* * *

Back in London, Gabriel took off his uniform for the last time. There were hardly any of the other officers on board when he left, and he departed as quietly as he had arrived nearly two years before.

As he drove out of the Royal Albert Dock he was sad to be leaving and that was a sensation he had not felt before.

Chapter 6

Next, Gabriel got himself a job in East Africa as part of a travelling team investigating disease patterns.

While the arrangements were being made for his transport to Africa he stayed with his parents in Dublin. Mrs Gabbett, who thought of Africa in terms of swamps, jungles and snakes, insisted on buying him a pair of gigantic lace-up boots which, though they required a considerable portion of his limited baggage space, he could not refuse to accept.

Eventually he was instructed to go to London to board an aircraft for Nairobi where he was to transfer to another flight to his new base in Mwanza on the southern shore of Lake Victoria.

He had never flown before and was a little apprehensive; a feeling not improved by a headline in his morning newspaper which read "Hermes Down in Desert." The story described a forced landing the previous day in West Africa of a sister aircraft of the type he was travelling in. It was disturbing reading but still, Gabriel reassured himself, it was unlikely that two Hermes planes would be forced down for any reason within a day of each other. Despite the apparent logic of this, his flight was blighted by a desire to have it over as quickly as possible. The flight was via Rome, Cairo and Khartoum. Here a new passenger boarded. He sat beside Gabriel and they exchanged nods in greeting, but did not speak to each other.

Gabriel had been reading Evelyn Waugh's *Scoop* and soon after leaving Khartoum reached the point in the story where the hero, William Boot, went to a department store to have himself kitted out for his journey to Africa and ended up buying items of completely useless equipment such as a humidor, a Santa Claus costume, and a cane for whacking snakes. On reaching this passage Gabriel laughed, thus causing the new passenger to regard him with some interest. Feeling that an explanation of his outburst was called for, Gabriel told the man why he was laughing. He seemed interested so Gabriel handed him the open book to read for himself, giving a brief resumé of what had gone before. The man took the book, spent some time reading it, handed it back and said, "I'm going to Northern Rhodesia. At present I'm selling firemen's helmets, but I deal generally in all sorts of mining equipment."

Reading the few paragraphs of the book had had no visible effect. He made no comment whatever about it, nor on Gabriel's reaction to it. He went on, "My firm makes all kinds of respirators, and gas masks too."

"Oh," said Gabriel.

"Yes," he continued, "we make a very wide range of articles like that. All to do with mining."

"Someone told me once," Gabriel interjected, "that the only people who consistently show a profit in mining are the people who make the equipment. Is there any truth in that?"

"Extractor fans, compressors, drills," the man droned on, "rescue equipment, everything. Would you like to see one?"

"See what?" asked Gabriel, not knowing if he was talking of fans or drills.

"A fireman's helmet," the man said, slightly piqued, regarding Gabriel as some sort of idiot.

"I don't mind," replied Gabriel, trying to convey, without being rude or provocative, that his interest in such articles was not intense.

The man leaned forward, reached under the seat in front of him, and pulled out a brown paper bag he had put there when he boarded. He opened it and produced a fireman's helmet which he put on his head. He pulled down the plastic visor over his face and turned towards Gabriel, "It's a very good fit," he said.

"Like a glove," agreed Gabriel who had been tempted to say, like a hat but thought better of it on the grounds that if Waugh had failed to make him laugh, what chance had he?

The salesman took off the helmet and handed it to Gabriel for his inspection in the meantime describing it in minute detail; the advantage of its shape, its quality and its low price. He talked interminably, and had Gabriel owned a mine, he would have bought anything to be rid of him.

Since his encounter with the man who knew he was a doctor on his first voyage from Dublin, Gabriel had met many of the type, in bars, hospitals, hotels and ships but this was his first meeting with the airborne bore. He was perfect, a collector's item, and Gabriel had to suffer him all the way to Nairobi.

After a night in the Norfolk Hotel Gabriel and two other passengers boarded a twin-engine plane for the last lap of the journey, and were soon winging towards the west, over miles of bush, across the Great Rift Valley to the shore of Lake Victoria. They landed on a grass runway and everyone got out. All the baggage was unloaded. Then the pilot asked Gabriel, "Aren't you going to Mwanza?"

"I am, yes."

"Well you'd better get back on board; this is only Musoma. We have another hundred miles to go."

Gabriel reloaded his bags and he and the pilot got back in the plane. They flew south, following the east coast of the lake until they descended towards another grass runway, at the side of which was a small corrugated iron shed with a motor van parked beside it.

The plane taxied to the shed and stopped. A man got out of the van. He was the agent of the local transport company and the pilot introduced him to Gabriel, saying, "This is Pete. He'll take care of you Doc."

"Yes, of course," said Pete. "Where are you going?"

"I haven't the faintest idea," answered Gabriel.

"I thought there'd be someone here to meet me. I'm supposed to be joining the staff of a medical laboratory here."

"I'd better take you to the hospital. There'll be someone there who'll know about you."

"Well I'm off," said the pilot. "Cheerio all."

It took about ten minutes to reach the hospital but they could find no one who knew anything about Gabriel. Eventually the matron suggested he might be joining the survey laboratory .

"That's right," said Gabriel, "but I can't understand why there's no one here to meet me."

"You take the doctor to the hotel, Pete," the Matron said, "and I'll ring the lab to tell him he'll be waiting there."

Gabriel spent the next half-hour sitting on the hotel verandah watching the passing parade in the street, and feeling lost and a little embarrassed to be holding a raincoat and umbrella in the sweltering heat. Presently an elderly man dressed in smart white shirt and very baggy shorts advanced on bandy legs towards him with outstretched hand, "Fanshawe, Admin," he said.

If only he'd said "Carruthers," Gabriel thought, hardly believing his eyes as he stood up and shook hands. "Dr Gabbett," he declared. "How do you do?"

"How do you do? We didn't expect you for months. What are you doing here?"

"I'm here because I got a letter telling me to come here, and a ticket to take me. They told me in London there was a great hurry to get out here."

"Not at all, old man, not at all. No hurry, no hurry. Glad to have you though. I've no idea what you're supposed to be doing, but we can sort that out later."

"Where am I staying?"

"You stay here in the hotel for a few days while we get a house ready for you. Go and register, freshen up, and have a meal. I'll come back in a few hours and put you in the picture. I'll bring the memsahib and we can all have a drink. OK?"

"OK by me. I'll see you later then."

When Fanshawe returned with his wife, whom he introduced as Helen, he led the way to the bar. With drinks safely in hand Gabriel was asked all the usual questions put to any newcomer, and gave an account of himself since he qualified. In his turn, Fanshawe told of how he and his wife had come to Tanganyika after the war. He had been in charge of a camel train in Kenya and Abyssinia delivering supplies to stations in the most remote places. He told Gabriel he must learn some Swahili. "Never forget to say *Jambo* to one and all. It's very important to exchange greetings with the natives. They are very polite people, and you will offend them if you are careless in these matters. You'll pick up enough of the local language in no time (I'll lend you some notes I made) but always try English first rather than make a fool of yourself trying to speak Swahili to a chap whose English is as good as your own. If you're stuck for a word in Swahili, particularly a noun, trying saying it in English but with an 'i' on the end of it, like *shillingi* for a shilling; it often works, but you must pronounce the 'i' like an 'e', the vowels have the same sounds as in Italian. You'll get the hang of it. All insects are *dudu*, all fly sprays are *flit,* all shoe polish *kiwi* all scouring powders for sinks and things are *vim,* and beer means beer, thank God, while whiskey already has an 'e' sound at the end."

After an hour of this, Gabriel was beginning to show signs of wear, and Helen slapped the old man on the knee and said, "Now that's enough for tonight. This lad's very tired after his trip."

Turning to Gabriel, she went on, "I'd better take the old bugger home, or he'll go on all night."

Gabriel was walking the couple to their car when Helen announced that she could not go on calling him "Gabriel."

"It's too much of a mouthful, and 'Gabby' is even worse. I'm going to call you 'Angel' in future, you know? After the Angel Gabriel. Hasn't anyone called you that before?"

"No," lied Gabriel, with a wistful smile and a happy twinge of memory, "never."

"Well from now on that's it," she said with authority. "Good night, we'll see you tomorrow. Come on Ted," she ordered Fanshawe, "let this lad get to bed."

"Cheerio, old man," said Fanshawe, "*kwa heri.*"

"Good night," answered Gabriel waving them on their way.

Angel Gabriel, he thought on his way upstairs to bed, Angel sounds all right. She's right, it is better than Gabriel.

***

Fanshawe took Gabriel to see his new house. It was about three miles outside the town on a

147

hillside overlooking the lake. It had two bedrooms, a sitting-room, dining-room, kitchen with electric cooker, a pantry, and, at the bottom of the back garden, a small house to accommodate a servant.

There was a short driveway leading to a garage at the side of the house, but it was impassable to cars because an outcrop of rock at least eighteen inches high protruded from the centre of it.

"We tried to move that," said Fanshawe, "but as the men dug around it they were unable to get to the edge of it. It's very big, like a bloody iceberg in fact, and it may go for miles in all directions. We may have to close off the drive and make another for you. We can't blast it, we'd break all the windows. I'll get the PWD chaps to have a look at it."

"What's that, the PWD?" asked Gabriel.

"The Public Works Department. They built the bloody thing in the first place, and didn't notice the rock until they'd finished. Can you believe that?"

Gabriel was not particularly interested in the rock, he had no car, nor any prospect of having one in the foreseeable future. He was far more concerned about how he was going to live in a house without any bedding or utensils. There was some heavy furniture: two beds with mattresses in each bedroom, a few chairs without cushions, some occasional tables, a dining table with six chairs to match, a sideboard, a porcelain water filter, but no refrigerator, floor covering nor curtains. He was thinking what to do when Fanshawe slapped him on the back and said,

"Well we'll go now and get you kitted out. We'll see about a car tomorrow."

"What car?"

"Oh you'll have to have a car. There's no other way of getting about."

"But I can't buy a car. It'll take me months to pay for the stuff for the house."

"That doesn't matter, old man. Old Patel won't expect to be paid for months and anyway they like to have you in debt to them. It's good for business. As far as a car is concerned, you can get an interest-free loan from the government which you pay back from your salary month by month over three years. It's not for nothing that people say that any bloody fool can get into the colonial service, but you have to be rich or very clever to get out again. Mind you, if you were either, you wouldn't join in the first place."

Old Patel turned out to be the proprietor of a large general store with the sign "Patel—Emporium" written over the door. With the help of a shop assistant and Fanshawe, Gabriel began buying things he needed to make the house habitable: saucepans, dishes, cutlery, everything for the kitchen, sheets, a blanket, pillows. There seemed no end to it.

"You can think about carpets later," Fanshawe said as they loaded the van, "but I think a small fridge is the top priority, unless you want to live out of cans."

Gabriel was thinking of nothing but his debts, telling himself he must have all this stuff.

Next, Fanshawe took him to the bank, introduced him to the manager, had an account opened, and told the cashier that the manager had authorised Gabriel to have a hundred pounds a month, or as he said it in the local currency, two thousand shillings, and would he be kind enough to cough up four hundred now. When all was done, the manager walked them to the door, where he took Gabriel's hand and said, "Anytime Doctor, anytime."

"That's the first time my bank manager has seen me to the door," Gabriel remarked to Fanshawe back in the van.

"That's because you have an overdraft, old man. He's just the same as Patel but he'd never admit it."

As they drove to the house, Fanshawe told Gabriel that he had received a letter from London which told him to expect a new doctor within a month or six weeks, and that the director of the laboratory would be returning in a month.

"But I met him at the Colonial Office before I left and he knew very well I was leaving for Mwanza the next day."

"I shouldn't try to work it out if I were you. You'll never get to the bottom of it. Half the time those chaps in London don't know what the hell is happening here, and it's just as well they don't, because if they did, they'd make an even bigger cock-up than they do already."

"What am I going to do till the boss arrives then?"

"Potter around the lab for a few hours a day. You could help train the microscopists for a while; there are specimens from the hospital to examine. You could spend the rest of the time getting to know the place and as many of the people you'll be working with as you can."

This appealed to Gabriel and he developed a routine. He spent the first hour or two of the morning walking or being driven round the town and the surrounding area and the remainder of the day in the laboratory. He adapted very rapidly to the life and before long ceased to feel himself a newcomer. He even hired a cook known as an *mpishi* who also looked after the house.

***

Gabriel heard voices one morning and, on looking out the window, was surprised to see a policeman, or *askari* sitting in the shade of a tree with a rifle resting across his knees, and, standing around the rock in the drive, four men dressed in off-white canvas shirts and shorts. The shirts were stamped all over with broad black arrows—convicts. So this is what old Fanshawe meant by the PWD, he thought. He dressed and went outside. When the *askari* saw him he jumped to his feet, gave a smart salute and said, "*Jambo, Bwana.*"

"*Jambo,*" answered Gabriel.

All the convicts said, "*Jambo.*"

"*Jambo,*" Gabriel said to them too.

The extent of Gabriel's Swahili allowed for no further conversation, so he returned inside for his breakfast. He could hear the men chatting and chanting together depending on the activity of the moment. They roared with laughter from time to time and the *mpishi* told Gabriel they were making rude and obscene remarks about him but he was too embarrassed to tell him what it was they were saying.

Watching from a window Gabriel saw the men dig around the rock to a depth of three feet; then they filled the hole with leaves, twigs and pieces of wood, and the *askari* set fire to the lot. As the fire blazed away they added fuel to it until the rock was completely covered. They kept the fire going for about an hour and finally, as it was dying down, they poured water over it. Immediately there was a cracking sound, and fissures appeared in the rock. More water was poured on until steam stopped rising; then they hit the rock with a sledge hammer breaking it into smaller pieces.

There was great satisfaction with the success of the work and the men were pleased with their efforts. They filled in the hole, and when they were finished shouted "*Kwa heri Bwana*" to Gabriel.

"*Asante sana, kwa heri,*" he replied.

They walked away carrying their shovels and hammers, followed by the *askari* holding the rifle across his shoulders, his arms draped over it.

***

Gabriel went to visit a leprosarium about a hundred miles south of Mwanza. He was driven by Abdallah, one of the laboratory drivers. The journey took three hours on a road which had transverse corrugations which caused the truck to rattle to such an extent that it seemed likely to fall apart. Abdallah told Gabriel that the faster you drove the better. Gabriel had his doubts about this but did not argue the point on the grounds that the faster they went the sooner the ordeal would be over.

The leprosarium consisted of a series of mud-and-wattle huts with palm frond or corrugated iron roofing, the whole compound being surrounded by a perimeter fence to keep out cattle and wild animals. Gabriel was welcomed by the doctor and his wife, and conducted on a tour of the wards, kitchen and workshops. The patients came from a wide area and exhibited leprosy in all its stages and types. Everyone able was engaged in work of some kind or in helping those incapable of looking after themselves. An air of love engendered by the doctor and his wife and all their assistants pervaded the place.

At the end of the tour the patients collected in one of the longer huts, the walls of which were only mud-plastered to about half their height so that more light and air entered. This was the assembly hall and at one end it had a raised stage to which the doctor led Gabriel. He raised his hand for silence, and told the people who Gabriel was, and then turning to him said, "Say a few words to them. I'll translate for you."

Gabriel was not prepared for this, and could only mumble a short speech of thanks for the welcome he had had. He then turned to go but the doctor told him to wait. "They're going to sing for you."

So he stood with his arms by his sides facing fifty or sixty patients as they sang to him. He noticed their wounds and deformities: the missing fingers, hands, feet, the terrible facial disfigurements, the contorted limbs, the ulcers, but through all this came joy and power as they sang. The concert lasted for ten minutes or so, and all Gabriel could say was, "*Asante sana, kwa heri,*" as the doctor led him from the stage. As tears rolled down his cheeks, he knew where he was and why he was there.

***

Gabriel was sent to Kenya to take charge of a field survey team consisting of himself, a nurse to help with the children and to question mothers on their childbearing histories and three laboratory technicians and microscopists to examine faeces and urine for parasites. Blood samples were collected for serological tests.

He had to close up his house and pack utensils he would need while living under canvas in Kenya. The field team was to work in the south west of the country about three hundred miles from Mwanza. Gabriel left, with Abdallah driving, on the first stage of the journey to Musoma the place he had thought was his final destination on his first day in Tanganyika. They drove on the road which follows the lake shore, crossing the Simiyu River on a ferry powered by the energy of two men pulling on wires spanning the river. They crossed the western edge of the Serengeti Plain where Gabriel had his first sight of the enormous herds of game and drove towards Baridi Hill to skirt its western end and continue to Musoma.

At the crest of a long slow hill the road forked at a gigantic mango tree. Their route was to the left; that to the right led to Benagi and Seronera and on to the Ngorongoro Crater, the heart of the big game country. Near the big tree they saw an old wartime jeep parked, and standing close to it, Sandy of the game department, whom Gabriel had met in Mwanza. They stopped and got out of the truck as Sandy crouched down to pump up a pressure stove. "*Jambo*," he greeted them, "tea, supper, dinner, or whatever you like to call it, will be served shortly."

"*Jambo*," said Gabriel and Abdallah. "We've arrived just in time."

Sandy finished pumping the stove, removed the pressure-cooker which had been resting on it, and replaced it with a kettle.

"This'll be ready as soon as it cools down a bit."

"What is it?" asked Gabriel.

"Stew. The best bloody stew in Africa, man. It has beef, mutton, goat, gazelle, garlic and chilli, potatoes, tomatoes, carrots, onions, beer and beans. Get yourselves plates."

As Gabriel and Abdallah got plates, Sandy opened a bottle of Burgundy.

"Where did you get that?" asked Gabriel.

"Patel's, where else?"

"No, that's not what I meant. How do you come to have such a thing on safari?"

"Why not?"

"Well it seems a bit much in the circumstances."

"Not at all, Angel old man. I like my plonk. So why shouldn't I have it whatever the circumstances? Just because you're away from home doesn't mean you have to go without. I take good care of myself. Some chaps travel around sleeping rough; no comfortable bed, no sheets. That's not for me. Any bloody fool can be uncomfortable on safari, but with a little effort, you can see everything with a rosy glow. Come on now; get glasses; get some of this down, and I'll open the cooker."

Soon they were enjoying the meal. Gabriel was enchanted as he thought of his good fortune to be eating so well in such beautiful surroundings. The glass of Burgundy was a master-stroke, he thought.

"God, this is marvellous, Sandy. How do you do it?"

"It's all very simple, old fruit. All you need is a stove and a pressure-cooker. You bung in a little water, any kind of meat you happen to have or can shoot, vegetables, garlic, spices, beer, anything in fact. You stew the lot until you think it's done. A little practice is all you need. A well-trained dog could do it."

"It's a stockpot in fact," said Gabriel, "and anyone who knows anything about food hygiene would condemn it at once."

"Don't be so bloody pompous, Angel; don't come the doctor lark; in a pressure-cooker the temperature is high enough to kill anything: it works like a sterilizer. I clean it out about once a week anyway. Do you want some more?"

"Shovel it out," said Gabriel.

When the meal was finished and everything packed away Sandy had to be off. "I'm after some poachers. Christ knows where they've got to but

I'm heading for Seronera as the most likely place. I'll see you back in Mwanza in three weeks."

"No you won't. We'll be in Kenya for at least three months."

"Well, I must get on, fellas. Seronera, shit or bust," he cried as he put the jeep into gear.

Gabriel and Abdallah went on to Musoma where they stayed overnight. The next morning they made another ferry crossing, of the Mara River to Kinesi. Two hours later they were at the field camp.

It is a simple matter to obtain a blood specimen from a patient, and most people can produce a urine sample without much trouble but getting a person to produce a stool to order is rather more difficult. Each patient was seen first by Gabriel who asked for name, village and age. Most of the people could only give an estimate of their age for it was not the custom to record dates of birth. Special "landmarks" were used in questioning to find out if an individual had been born, say, before the first World War and often important local events could be used in the same way. On asking a youth his name, the boy answered, "Hitler."

"Hitler?" queried Gabriel.

"Yes, Bwana, Hitler."

Gabriel asked his mother if this were truly the boy's name.

"Yes Bwana, we called him Hitler because he was born the day the war began."

So Gabriel had a precise date of birth. He had a little trouble with Hitler though; he had not produced a stool, and when Gabriel had finished examining him, he gave him a container and asked him to try again. The boy returned an hour later holding two full containers which he handed to Gabriel, "This one is mine," he said, indicating his right hand; "and the other is my brother's."

"Good, *asante*," said Gabriel.

As the boy turned away he exchanged a glance with one of his friends and smirked. Gabriel, his suspicions aroused, asked one of the technicians to investigate, and was told later that people who could not produce the necessary sample to order were helped out by others with an abundant supply.

"How long has this been going on?" he demanded to know.

"I don't know Doctor but it could have been happening since we started here."

"No wonder we get a specimen from nearly everyone, one bloke could supply at least a dozen others. This'll make a fine bloody mess of our statistics. I suppose they've been sharing out the pee as well?"

"I don't think so Doctor, anyone can produce that fairly easily."

"Well there's nothing we can do about it now. Ask the Chief to tell them to stop it, and that they mustn't be afraid to tell us if they can't supply everything we ask for. It's a bloody tall order however you look at it."

Gabriel and the team completed the survey without further incident until the day before they were due to leave. A mother brought her ill baby for help. The infant had pneumonia and was near to death. If the child was to have any chance of survival, hospital treatment was the only hope. The nearest hospital was at least ten miles away. Gabriel took them in the truck, the woman beside him, the baby in her arms panting his life away. As they drove into the hospital compound, the baby died. Gabriel turned the lorry around to take them home, but the woman said she wanted to go to friends in the town, "*Asante sana Bwana,*" she said, as she walked away with the baby tightly held to her. After taking a few steps, she stopped, turned to him again and said, "*Asante sana Bwana, kwa heri.*"

She had no tears in her eyes, at least not to show him. Then she lowered her eyes to look at the baby and started to walk away again.

The team was deeply moved by this event—the effect of proximate death. In another part of Kenya at that time the Mau Mau campaign was at its height, and violent deaths were a daily occurrence; they were remote and hardly impinged on their consciousness at all.

Chapter 7

Gabriel spent the next year with a team in Tanganyika, and then returned to Kenya to work among the Digo people on the coast south of Mombasa.

This time, Gabriel had his cook-cum-general-servant, Wilson, with him.

At the site there were two small huts, and these along with several tents comprised the accommodation. The laboratory was set up in a third hut some distance from the main site.

On leaving for Mombasa, the laboratory director told Gabriel that the Chief of the villages in the survey had five headmen, one for each village, and that the order in which the work was to be done would be determined by lot after he had had discussions with a statistician in Nairobi. He would send a signal (he never said "telegram") to Gabriel advising him of the result of their deliberations after the team's arrival at the Coast.

Being in Mombasa again gave Gabriel the same feeling he got when looking at the sea from Killiney Hill; a sense of belonging, perhaps of being at home. As the dried-up hinterland merged into the lush greenery of the coast, and he saw the harbour and ships below him, there was nowhere else he wanted to be.

The location of the campsite was perfect—on a patch of open ground leading by way of a six-foot high coral bank to the ocean a few yards below. There was a cooling breeze, and the noise of the surf mingled with the sound of drumming from the nearby village and the rattling of the palm trees. At the end of the first day Gabriel went for a swim in the lagoon. As he floated on his back with his eyes shut, he thought, tropical paradise, Jasus, and they're paying me too!

The next morning he and the team nurse, known to all as Sister Suzie, went to visit the Chief. On the way she said, "Thank God, my seat fits the latrine."

"What do you mean?" asked Gabriel, surprised.

"My seat fits the latrine, that's all. I never go anywhere without it."

"I hope not. What seat? What the hell are you talking about? You're not that broad in the beam."

"Now don't be silly, Angel. My lavatory seat, I mean. I never go anywhere without it. It's mahogany, and I've carried it throughout East Africa for over thirty years. I believe in keeping up standards of comfort; it doesn't take much effort. You can borrow it if you like."

"Well I've heard everything. Even William Boot didn't have a lav seat."

"William Boot, who's he?"

"I'll tell you some other time. We've arrived."

The Chief was standing at the door of his house waiting for them. He was a heavily-built man with a great smiling face. He was dressed in the long white nightshirt-like cotton garment universal in the Muslim world, which is called a *kanzu* in Kiswahili. On his head he wore a small white skullcap or *kofia*. He had a black lumpy umbrella hung on his arm. He greeted Gabriel and the nurse, and sent a little boy to get some chairs.

When they were seated, Gabriel explained in detail what the team hoped to do. The Chief said that the people who lived close by the camp would come to be examined, but that those from more distant villages would not. He agreed to hold a meeting, or *baraza*, at which all the headmen and the elders of the villages would be told of their plans and they would then decide on the degree of cooperation there would be.

In the several days it took to arrange the meeting, Gabriel and the others unpacked the equipment and arranged everything ready for the work to commence.

At the *baraza* there were about fifty men present but no women. The Chief started by explaining the presence of Gabriel and the team and the purpose of the medical examinations and tests that they wanted to do. When he had finished, the discussion began. It continued for an hour, Gabriel understanding nothing of what was being said. He was ignored except when someone deigned to nod in his direction or to point at him from time to time.

Finally, when everyone had had his say, the Chief told Gabriel that agreement had been reached that instructions be given to the women to have their children examined. This disappointed

Gabriel but at least he felt some good could be done if the children were seen. "Let me know which headman's village you want to start with," the Chief told him, "and I'll tell him to send his people to you?"

Before leaving, Gabriel asked the Chief if he knew of anyone whom he could employ as an interpreter. The Chief said he would find someone and ask him to go along to the campsite.

Gabriel telegraphed headquarters for instructions regarding the choice of headman. The answer came back: "First headman Sudi chosen."

He went to the Chief and told him he would like to start with first headman Sudi's people. A blank look came over the Chief's face. "I don't know any man called Sudi?" he said.

"Well he must be here somewhere," insisted Gabriel.

"No Bwana, there is no one here of that name?"

Gabriel sent another telegram, and received in reply: "First signal corrupt repeat corrupt stop First headman should be chosen."

He went to see the Chief again. "It seems," he said, "that the word 'Sudi' that I read as a man's name should have read 'should be.' So all we need to do is to tell the first headman."

"Who's he?" asked the puzzled Chief.

"How the hell should I know?" snapped Gabriel. "They're your bloody headmen."

"I know I have five headmen?" said the Chief, responding to Gabriel's impatience with a tone somewhat abrupt, "but they don't have numbers, first, second, third. I don't know what all this means."

163

"You're not the only one. We'll just pick the one who lives nearest our camp. Who's he?"

"Bwana Jumaa bin Ali."

"Good. Tell him he's elected and ask him to come to see me tomorrow."

"Very well Bwana I'll tell him." and the Chief walked away shaking his head in the manner of a man who recognized lunacy when he saw it.

On the day the work started a small crowd gathered in the shade of the laboratory made up of women, young children and a few curious youths. Gabriel was preparing for the first patient when a young man appeared. He had on a white shirt and blue trousers and wore battered old brown shoes. "*Jambo* Bwana," he said. "I am Rashidi bin Khamis and I speaks English. The Chief is sending me to you."

As he spoke he held out his right hand, at the same time clasping his forearm just above the wrist with the other. Gabriel shook the proffered hand. "Jambo Rashidi, are you going to be my interpreter?"

"Yes, Doctor. I am Mdigo and knows these people well."

"Have you ever worked in a hospital or laboratory before?"

"No, Doctor. I was being a driver, but the job gaves me a backache."

"Never mind. All you'll have to do here is help me to understand what the patients are saying and, of course, help them to understand me. Later on, if you like, we can show you how to use a microscope. It'd make things more interesting for you."

"Very good Doctor. I am starting now?"

"Yes, why not? Ask the first woman to come in please?"

Gabriel carried out his standard examination, and wrote down his findings. Rashidi proved himself an excellent interpreter and explained to each woman what was being done. They examined about twenty people before stopping for their midday meal. The rest of the time was spent in examining the samples collected during the morning. This pattern was followed for several weeks but in that time only a very small number of men came. Rashidi told Gabriel, "They are not coming, because they are not believing you can do anything to help them. Most of the people here are knowing already what is wrong with them. It's the hookworms and malaria—things like that. If they were having any money they are helping themselves but there are no jobs here, and there is nothing to do for them."

He was right, and Gabriel knew it, but he believed that by knowing as much as possible about disease patterns the government would be better informed on what action needed to be taken. He had serious doubts though about the value of all this work, as any effective action would require millions of pounds to be spent. The real problems were poverty and ignorance, and the primary requisite to attack these was money, and he concluded that the only worth of his presence was the collection of statistics. He could see no dividend for the individuals who came to see him. He felt he was deceiving them in raising their hopes of improvement.

As the weeks became months Gabriel and Rashidi got to know each other very well, and after the day's work went goggling in the lagoon to watch the fish in the clear water. Rashidi always left before dark to cycle home to his wife and two children. At weekends he came to talk. "I have come for conversations," he announced on the first occasion he appeared at Gabriel's tent late one afternoon. He had told Gabriel he was the first European he had ever spoken to, apart from saying *Jambo* now and again. Whenever he arrived he shook hands, but always holding his wrist with his left hand. Gabriel had noticed that he did not do this when he shook hands with another African and when asked why this was so, Rashidi was reluctant to tell him and began talking about something else. Gabriel persisted and eventually Rashidi told him it was to stop the poison going up his arm.

"What poison?" Gabriel asked.

"It's the magic Doctor. You could do harm to me, even though you are not meaning to. I am stopping it by holding my wrist?"

"How do you mean?"

"Well there may be something bad in you which is harming me, so I stops it."

Gabriel could get no better explanation but the incident served to illustrate the cultural gulf between them. No matter how well they knew each other, no matter what degree of trust developed, there would always be an insurmountable barrier. This was how Rashidi saw a European, even when he granted that his presence was intended to bring no harm to him.

"Does everybody feel like that?" Gabriel asked.

"Oh yes Doctor," Rashidi laughed, "they all does."

"Do you think Africans will ever trust us?"

"No Doctor, they never will. Do you know a European who is trusting us?"

"I trust you."

"And I trusts you."

"Yes, but you still believe I can poison you just by grasping your hand?"

Rashidi did not answer. He laughed again and changed the subject. "I wants your advice Doctor."

"What about?"

"My wife has returned to her father."

"Is she leaving you? Is she divorcing you?"

"No. At least I doesn't think so, but she may not be coming back for a long time."

"Has she ever gone back to her father before?"

"No."

"Well maybe she'll be back in a few days. Why do you think she has left you?"

"It's because I am saying I wants a second wife, and she is not liking that."

"I don't blame her. How would you like it if she wanted another husband?"

"She couldn't do that."

"Why not?"

"Because I'm the man."

"I don't see what difference that makes. You want to have things all your own way."

"I wants another wife and I am knowing two girls I am liking and I wants you to tell me which one I should have."

"I can't possibly do that, and anyway I don't know either of them. What are they like? Which one do you love?"

"I loves the two of them Doctor but one is very good in the face."

"Well if you love both of them, I suppose you should have the better looking one."

"Yes that's what I am thinking too but I should not marry her."

"Why not?"

"Because she's able to ride a bicycle."

"Able to ride a bicycle? What in heaven's name has being able to ride a bicycle got to do with it?"

"Aah," Rashidi said, leaning forward with a knowing smile and wagging a finger at Gabriel, "I has a bike."

Gabriel was about to preach to him for being so selfish in deciding in advance that he was not prepared to lend the bicycle, even to his wife, when they heard groaning coming from outside the tent. Rashidi went out to see what was happening. Gabriel heard him talking for a few minutes before he returned to tell him there was a man outside who had been in a fight and was injured. Gabriel could see in the dim light a man wearing a cap on the side of his head.

"*Jambo*, Bwana," he said coming in.

"*Jambo*," answered Gabriel, "what's the matter?"

"I was hit on the head with a machete and it hurts."

"Come closer to the light and take off your cap. Let's have a look."

"What cap?" the man asked.

It was then that Gabriel was able to see he was not wearing a cap and what he had taken for one was in fact the skin and hair of the man's scalp which had been cut and pulled down over his ear by a glancing blow. The wound was quite clean and the bleeding had stopped. Gabriel sat the man down to inspect the wound closely and then returned the skin flap to its proper position.

"I'll take you to the hospital in Mombasa in the morning. You'll need some stitches in this. Come early so we'll catch the first Likoni ferry."

"Yes Bwana," the man said, "*asante sana.*"

Gabriel wound a bandage around his head and gave him a few aspirin tablets. The man did not return the next day but Rashidi told Gabriel he had come to his house to say that he did not want to have stitches and that he was going to work."

"What does he work at?"

"He cuts the sugar canes, Doctor."

"Well I'll bet he has a sore head today. When you see him again ask him to come here. I'd like to see how he gets on."

Two weeks later he returned. The wound had healed very well though the scar was wider than it need have been. The man had no complaint and said he was very well. He gave Gabriel a present of three eggs wrapped in a cloth. "These are your gift, Doctor," he said.

***

Rashidi was a Muslim and had received religious instruction at a village school. Thie consisted of little groups of children sitting around a teacher chanting the Koran for a few hours every day.

All Gabriel knew about religion was what had been drummed into him at school in Dublin and there, no mention of any other religion was made, except for it to be dismissed as heretical, schismatic, non-Christian or pagan. Catholicism was the one, true church and "no one can be saved out of it?" They had been told regularly that Martin Luther was mad. In the years since leaving school Gabriel had had the opportunity to visit many mission stations of various denominations. They all impressed him with the intensity of their endeavours and their devotion to God and man.

As for the Catholic priests and nuns he came to know, what a different lot they were to the ones he had left in Ireland! Here was the real Church Militant working on a foundation of love; in Ireland was the Church Comfortable, resting on foundations of arrogance, power and the instillation of fear.

Whatever inhibitory effects religion had on Gabriel, it had none on Rashidi. He was a tomcat and according to his own accounts that was the most apt description of his behaviour. He was an accomplished adulterer but when Gabriel told him that that was how he saw him, he only laughed and said, "But I'm a *man*, Doctor, I'm a *man!*"

"All the more reason why you should be faithful to your wife and not behave like an animal!" declared Gabriel with the smug arrogance of the doctrinaire.

"Everybody does it, Doctor, everybody. There's no trouble as long as you doesn't get found out."

"As long as you are not found out," corrected Gabriel.

"What?"

Gabriel explained how he should have made up the sentence.

"I knows Doctor. My verbs is the worst. I never does them properly but I am speaking English very well otherwise?"

Gabriel agreed. Allowing that Rashidi very rarely expressed his tenses correctly, he had an excellent command of English and it was because of this that Gabriel was able to understand his background so well and came also to know much of the local tribal history and of the attitudes of the people towards Europeans and colonialism.

During the fasting month of Ramadan, Rashidi abstained from all food and drink from sunrise to sunset—at least he said he did when Gabriel challenged him with the idea that he might be eating and drinking alone. At the end of the month, at the first sighting of the new moon, the villagers had a celebration feast and, on his way to one of these, Rashidi called to see Gabriel. He was no longer wearing his familiar shirt and trousers but had a new white *kanzu* and a red fez.

"*Jambo*, Doctor," he said as he turned around to show himself off, "how do you thinks I look?"

"Very smart, very smart. Would you like a beer to celebrate?"

"*Asante sana*. I loves beer."

"I thought alcohol was forbidden to Muslims."

"I knows that Doctor, but you're not a Muslim."

"So what? It all boils down to the fact that as long as another Muslim doesn't see what you're

171

up to, it doesn't matter, and you can do what you like."

Rashidi thought for a moment before answering and then said, "The God knows what I does, Doctor, and he knows that I'm not a bad man. He made me and he knows what I does. What I does may be bad, but it's only the religion that says so. I'm not bad with the God, Doctor."

"What do you think he'll do to you when you die?"

"The Koran is saying that the God is merciful; he won't put me in the fire. He's letting me in the paradise."

"I wouldn't be too sure of that if I were you. What's this paradise like?"

"Oh very good, very nice."

"Tell me about it."

"Well when I dies I'm going to the heaven and an angel is greeting me. He will say, '*Jambo* Rashidi,' and I will answer, '*Jambo*, Bwana.' Then he will tell me the God is forgiving me and that I am to come in. Everything will be very beautiful with tall trees shading me from the sun. There will be bright green grass with a cool river flowing from a snowy mountain into a pool for me to bathe in. There will be beautiful flowers of all colours, and trees having sweet fruits for me to eat, and there will be honey from the bees. All the birds will sing, not like the birds we are having here, many looking nice, but only a few singing. The birds of heaven will sing, Doctor."

Rashidi stopped his narrative to say that he had heard that in Europe there were lots of birds able to sing sweetly. Gabriel confirmed there were, but that that did not make Europe more heavenly than Africa. "But never mind that," he said. "Go on."

"That's nearly everything, except for the girls. There will be four of them all willing to do anything I wants with me and no one of them will know that the other ones is there."

"What do you mean?" queried Gabriel.

"I will be seeing four girls but each of them will only be able to see me and the heaven but not the other three girls."

"What's the point of that?"

"If each one believes that they have me alone they are not being jealous and so are not fighting over me."

"You have a hell of an opinion of yourself," protested Gabriel.

"But I'm the *man*, Doctor," insisted Rashidi, and as far as he was concerned there was no more to be said.

"Your idea of heaven is very appealing but don't you think you'd get tired of it, if it went on just like that forever?"

"No. The God will take care of that. I won't feel that it is going on forever."

"There's an answer for everything. I think I'd be bored stiff."

"What do you think will happen to you when you dies, Doctor?"

"I don't know but I'm supposed to enjoy the Beatific Vision. That is, I shall see God."

"Oh I don't see the God, only angels. But what are you doing after you see him?"

"I don't know."

"Well I knows what will happen to me," Rashidi declared with great assurance; then asked, "Why do you want to go to heaven if you doesn't know what will happen there?"

"Because I don't want to go to hell, the fire as you call it."

"How is it that you knows what the hell is like but you doesn't know about the heaven?"

"A good question," admitted Gabriel. "I suppose we know what suffering is, so we can visualize hell but we cannot imagine true happiness, so a definition of heaven eludes us."

"Yes, I suppose you're right. I've never had true happiness. I thought I was being happy when I married but since my children came I found out that I had never known what real worry was before. Anyway I knows what I like doing best and if the heaven is what I expect I am being happy there."

They sat silently for some time before Rashidi asked, "How does anyone know what will happen to us?"

"No one does. They only think they do. They want to believe what the theologians tell them, so they do."

"Theo—what? What is that?"

"Theologians. They are people who study God and his ways or at least they study what other theologians say or have written but no one really *knows*. It's like placing your head between two mirrors and seeing reflections reflecting reflections on and on. Theologians are people that speculate on the speculations of other speculators and at the end of the life of each one of them, they *know* no more than those who have gone before."

"It's their nonsense. I just believes in the God."

"That's it, Rashidi. Just believe despite them all and hope for the best, using free will with love."

"Very good. That's what I'm doing. I'm going to the dances now, and there'll be plenty of girls there to love."

He jumped up, gave a knowing wink, finished his beer and gathered his *kanzu* up to his knees. "I doesn't need trousers with a *kanzu*," he said as he set off at a trot.

***

Gabriel and Rashidi went to the Tsavo National Park at Voi to see elephants. Rashidi was quite overawed by their size and, in order to communicate some idea of this to his friends at home, collected the biggest turd he could find, nearly as big as a football, which he wrapped in a copy of the *Mombasa Times*.

"Put that thing in the boot," Gabriel ordered. "It'll stink out the car."

"No one is believing me when I tells them the size of an elephant," Rashidi told him, "but when I shows them that, and tells them that it is only a small piece, they'll have to. Won't they?"

"A picture is worth a thousand words," said Gabriel.

On their arrival back in Mombasa they drove to Kilindini Harbour for Gabriel to show Rashidi over his old ship which was on one of its regular visits. On the way out through the dock gates they had to stop for customs examination. The young man on duty wanted to look in the boot of the car. It was empty except for the spare wheel and a few tools. And, of course, the parcel. "What's in that?" he asked Rashidi.

"Elephant shit."

There was silence for a few moments and Gabriel was about to get out to explain.

"What did you say?"

"Elephant shit," repeated Rashidi.

The man shut the lid of the boot, walked to Gabriel's side of the car and said, "At least that's a change from the usual bullshit," and waved them through the gate.

Chapter 8

Gabriel's work on the Coast was to take several more months, but plans for his next venture had to be made well in advance. In order to do this he arranged to drive to Tanga to discuss with local officials the possibility of setting up camp near there. Rashidi was supposed to go with him but did not arrive in time and Gabriel left without him. He travelled on a little-used road which in places was no more than a sandy track.

With his Tanga business finished he returned by the same route but on attempting to drive across a deep sandy patch, which had given him no trouble in the morning, the car became stuck. He was unable to get it going again by himself and became very frustrated, and furious with Rashidi for having failed to accompany him.

He knew that no more than a dozen cars a week used the road, so he decided to start walking in the direction he had been going, reckoning that the camp was about ten miles further on and that he should be able to reach it before nightfall. He had covered about two miles when he came across piles of fresh elephant dung. This frightened him;

elephants can be extremely dangerous, and he was defenceless. He stopped to listen, and hearing nothing started walking again. He had hardly recovered from his fright when just a yard or two ahead of him a large male baboon appeared from the dense bush bordering the road. Gabriel was terror-struck and felt rooted where he stood. The baboon stopped too and glared at him. Gabriel thought, if he attacks me I'm dead. There was nothing he could do. If he ran the animal might run after him. While these thoughts chased through his brain the rest of the baboon's troop came out of the bush and crossed the road. The big male kept watching Gabriel until the last one had gone into the bush; then he too followed, grunting as he went.

Gabriel felt weak at the knees, but started to walk on again, beginning to feel thirsty. He had thoughts of the possibility of not reaching the camp before dark, and even of never reaching it at all. He knew there were lions also in the area. Christ, he thought, is this how I'm going to die?

As he walked on bitter feelings towards Rashidi developed for having let him down. I'll kill that bastard, he thought, if he'd been with me, we'd have had that bloody car on the move again in a couple of minutes.

He came to a small village he did not know existed. A few youths came towards him. "*Jambo*, Bwana" they said.

"*Jambo*," croaked Gabriel.

"What are you doing here? Where's your car?"

Gabriel did not answer but just asked for some water. One of the boys returned with a tumbler filled with a dark muddy liquid. Gabriel drank it all in a gulp and asked for another, despite his conscious thought of the risk of typhoid fever. He began to feel better and told the boys what had happened and of his encounter with the baboons. They considered the whole event a great joke, and went into gales of laughter as they re-enacted it, one of them taking the part of Gabriel, as he shook himself in mock fear.

Eventually, one of them asked how far away the car was, and told Gabriel they expected a bus from Mombasa to arrive soon. When it came Gabriel and the boys got in and returned to the car and, with everyone shoving, it was out of the sand in no time. Back at the village Gabriel thanked everyone and gave the boys a pound. They gave him a bunch of bananas, "in case you meet any more baboons," they told him.

When he arrived back at the camp, Gabriel sent for Wilson. "Where's that bastard Rashidi?" he asked.

"I don't know, Bwana, he hasn't been here all day."

Gabriel had to wait until the following morning to vent his spleen. Rashidi arrived at the usual time. When Gabriel saw him he charged towards him and snarled, "Where the hell were you yesterday? I got stuck in sand and had to walk miles. I nearly met a herd of elephants, and a baboon could have killed me. What the bloody hell were you doing?"

Before Gabriel could continue, Rashidi looked blandly at him and said, "*Jambo*, Bwana."

"*Jambo*, my arse," screamed Gabriel, "where were you?"

"*Jambo*, Bwana," Rashidi repeated, and added, "I'm greeting you, Doctor, and you must greets me."

"I'll greet you with a poke in the nose if you don't tell me what you were doing yesterday."

"Oh, I couldn't come yesterday. I was to get my wife back from her father's. I thought you were being all right without me."

Gabriel told him again what had happened to him, and finished by saying, "Don't you realise that I could have been killed, or have died of thirst? I've finished with you. I have a good mind to get rid of you now but I'll give you just one chance. Do you understand that?"

"Yes, Doctor."

"So any more trouble and you're sacked. Right?"

"No, Doctor."

"What do you mean 'no Doctor'?"

Gabriel had not been looking at Rashidi while delivering his diatribe but now he did and saw he had tears in his eyes.

"What do you mean?" he asked again, more quietly, "by 'no Doctor?'"

"You can't sacks me."

"Why not? Why can't I sack you?"

"Because I loves you Doctor." Then he lowered his head, began to walk away but turned and looked directly at Gabriel, "and you loves me," he said.

***

On occasion Gabriel spent weekends with an old retired tea planter, Charles, who lived in Shimoni, a small fishing village a few miles south of his campsite. Charles owned a large out-rigger canoe or *ngalawa* in which they went sailing or fishing. Shimoni is separated from the ocean by Wasin, a low-lying coral island about a mile off-shore, whose main feature was an enormous baobab tree which marked its western tip. The island shelters Shimoni and thus provides a safe anchorage for trading dhows from Arabia which call on their way south or north depending on the monsoon winds.

Charles had his own petrol-driven generator which enabled him to have a record player and amplifiers. His favourite record was of Beethoven's "Emperor" concerto.

In the relative coolness of the early tropical morning as the night brightened before the sun's rising over the sea, the powerful sounds of piano and orchestra could be heard across the water on the anchored dhows. As they prepared to go to sea one of the sailors beat a drum as the others hoisted the sail—the ageless custom of drumming up a wind. To stand at the water's edge, to look and listen as the drummer blended his rhythm to that of the music, to watch the lateen sail rise and wave as the wind began to rise, brought to Gabriel a sense of knowing that at that instant all that was worth having was his.

* * *

With the work finished all the equipment was packed and the team returned to Mwanza. Rashidi decided that he wanted to train as a microscopist so he went too.

The team were next in western Tanganyika to complete a project which had been suspended because the previous group had been accused by a witch doctor of drinking some of the blood collected from local people. The accusation arose after someone had been seen putting tomato ketchup on his food.

The site of operations was in the hills near Kasula, about thirty-five miles east of Lake Tanganyika. Gabriel, a technician named Colin, and Sister Suzie shared a three-roomed brick hut. On their first evening as they were unpacking Wilson came to the door, leaned on the door-post with one leg crossed over the other, dropped a lid over a languid eye and asked, "What's for dinner?"

"You're the bloody cook, find something," Gabriel told him.

"There's a chicken outside no one seems to own. Will that do?"

"Yes, get on with it."

Wilson cooked the bird in the pressure-cooker which was intended to be a sterilizer for the needles and syringes used in the blood sampling but if they were placed in the top compartment of the cooker no juices from the food would contaminate the instruments.

Later, Gabriel, Suzie and Colin were drinking coffee outside the house when Suzie said, "It's at this time of the day that I miss my hubby most of all. We often sat outside our tent while he played the piano."

"Played the what?" asked Gabriel incredulously.

"The piano," she repeated, and went on, "you can doubt me if you like but in those days we always took the piano with us on safari. Nowadays you are limited to what you can get in a truck but in those days whatever you wanted to take, you took— you just ordered a few more porters and off you went."

"Well," said Gabriel, "I've heard of the White Man's burden, but this is the first I've heard of the Black Man's ditto."

"When I talk of the good old days," said Sister Suzie, "that's what I mean. Things were better then—for all of us. You mark my words, Sonny Angel."

"The Africans I talk to would give you an argument there, I'm afraid but we needn't go into that now."

"I want you to do something for me," Suzie said, changing the subject.

"Yes, what is it?"

"If ever anything happens to me."

"Yes, of course we will. What do you want us to do?"

"I want to be buried beside my husband."

"Sure. We'll do that for you all right. Are you thinking of moving on then?"

"No, be serious for a minute," she ordered, slapping the back of his hand.

"All right, where is your husband buried, and how do we go about arranging things for you?"

"He's not buried yet," she said. "I had him cremated and his ashes are in a cigar box in the pocket of my brown swagger coat hanging in the wardrobe in our house in Tanga."

"Now who's not being serious?" asked Gabriel.

"But I am," she insisted, "and that's the truth. You are to contact my bank. They'll be my executors and they'll know what to do. Will you do that for me?"

"Sure we will, or at least one of us will, whoever happens to be around when you hang up your thermometer but you haven't told us where you're to be buried."

"Tanga will do or you can send the cigar box and have that buried wherever they've laid me. That might be easier, and you wouldn't have the bother of having me cremated in order to send the ashes to Tanga."

"Very good," said Colin, who had remained silent until now. "Leave it to us: Burnem and Buryem, Undertakers."

They drank some more coffee before retiring for the night.

The next morning Sister Suzie remained at the house to write up her reports while the others went to see the patients. On the way, Gabriel asked Colin if he believed what Suzie had told them about her husband's ashes being in a cigar box.

"Believe it?" cried Colin, "I was bloody well with her when she put them in."

"Tell me about it."

"We were out in the bush," Colin began, "in the back of beyond, when her husband died suddenly. We wanted to bury him there and then, but she would not hear of it. Instead, she wanted him taken to Tanga where they lived. We were miles from there and we had no way of transporting a body such a distance in this climate. We wrapped him in a sheet and put him in the back of the truck and drove to a place near Arusha where there was a PWD dépôt. She asked the foreman if he would cremate the remains but he was horrified at the idea. She was very determined though and the foreman suggested she ask the local Hindu priest, or whatever he is, to do it. He agreed, and the job was done."

"Then what happened?"

"When everything was finished, Suzie and some other old girl poked around in the remains of the pyre trying to determine which parts were bits of wood and which the departed. After a while they had chosen enough to fill a biscuit tin."

"We then drove to Nairobi and booked in at the Norfolk. Suzie decided that the quantity of material she had was much more than there should have been, so she spilled the lot on to a newspaper spread out before the fire in the sitting-room and picked out the bits she believed were parts of her old man. Finally, the quantity was reduced to what would fill a cigar box she cadged from the barman. She wrapped up what was left and put it in the fire. The next day her son came to take her home."

Gabriel had listened in silence to the story and then said, "You're having me on."

"No I'm not. It's the gospel truth and after the performance I witnessed, I have no doubt that what's left of the old boy *is* in the pocket of her swagger coat in Tanga."

Before finishing at Kasulu, Gabriel and Rashidi went to Kigoma, the town at the end of the railway from Dar es Salaam on the eastern shore of Lake Tanganyika. A short distance south of Kigoma is the village of Ujiji, the place where Stanley found Livingstone in 1871. The meeting is commemorated by a dressed stone monument which has an outline map of Africa, on which is superimposed a cross. At one side there is a metal plaque recording the event.

As Gabriel read the inscription he thought of a far off day in Rathmines when his grandfather had given him the little book on African exploration, and here he was standing at the site of Stanley's meeting with Livingstone nearly a hundred years before. The book related how Stanley, with the American flag flying at the head of his line of porters, met Livingstone. The doctor looked pale, Stanley recorded. He was wearing an old blue cap with a faded gold band around it. He had a red-sleeved waistcoat and grey trousers. Stanley went up to him, raised his hat, and said, "Dr Livingstone, I presume?"

"It's just like the history at school," Rashidi remarked.

Gabriel knew what he meant; he also had this sense of living in history. There was a reality in this moment; dramatic and romantic.

"Did he do any good, Rashidi?"

"I thinks he did. He was helping to stop the slavery."

"Yes. I suppose if he did nothing else he did at least do that. I often wonder if any foreigner does any good here. What good do I do? I have reached the stage where I feel the work I'm doing is of little value and that it would be better if I were to do ordinary doctoring—just caring for sick people in one place."

"But that's it. The government gets its money from the taxes it raises, only the people can make money.

"It's odd to think though that Livingstone was fighting slavery when you consider that it had contributed in a big way to Britain's wealth in the past."

"How do you mean?"

"Well it was one of the things that made Britain the richest country in the world: sugar, slaves, steam, steel and seamanship. These together made it great."

They took each other's photograph before leaving Ujiji. As they drove towards their campsite they saw a pall of thick grey smoke hang over everything and as they came closer saw that the hut beside the main one was ablaze. It was made of wooden poles and covered all over, roof and walls, in grass thatching. It had two sections, one was Wilson's room, the other the camp kitchen.

Gabriel could see no sign of Wilson as he jumped out of the car. He ran to the back of the blazing hut, and found him running about waving his arms like a hen beating the air. When he saw Gabriel he ran towards him smiling broadly and, pointing at his head said, "*Jambo*, Bwana, my hat's all right."

"How did this happen?" Gabriel roared over the noise of the fire.

"The iron did it," shouted Wilson. "A piece of charcoal fell out and the flames came at once but I got my hat out?"

The hat was a cherished possession bought only a few days previously in Kasulu.

"You and your bloody hat," complained Gabriel. "Where's all my stuff?"

"Gone, Bwana. I couldn't do anything."

"You managed to save that bloody hat but lost all my shirts and the kitchen things."

"I was wearing the hat when the fire started. I wasn't able to get back in to save anything else."

When the fire had burnt itself out, they rummaged around the débris to see what could be salvaged. They got nothing and were left with only what had been outside: the pressure-cooker and a saucepan, some cutlery and a few plates. As their work was all but complete they returned to Mwanza the next day.

***

Gabriel was now due for his first home leave, and made his preparations to return to Europe.

His pleasure at seeing his parents and family was soon replaced by a sense of boredom. His thoughts were centred on the people he had left, on the Rift Valley, the ocean at Mombasa, the lake. Though he had doubts about the value of his work, he could not wait to return to it. But before he could do that he had six months leave to spend. He went to the Continent: France, Italy, Austria, Germany. All very beautiful, he thought, but not a patch on the Serengeti for all their fine buildings and treasures.

At last it was time to go back and he had to be careful not to appear too pleased at severing once again the chains of kinship that held him like a rubber band, though one of infinite elasticity.

He travelled by sea, and had the pleasure of being blasé about Port Said and the Canal. He had to be careful to be reticent in offering hints or advice for fear of become a bore; a type he was quick to detect and now adept at avoiding.

On his arrival at Mombasa he was rejoined by Rashidi and together they left for Lake Victoria in the new car Gabriel had brought with him.

On reaching his house, Gabriel could find no trace of Wilson. He had gone to Uganda, he heard, and had not been seen since. A man named Omari wanted the job. "I would like to work for you Bwana," he said, "because you have no wife."

"What's that got to do with it?" Gabriel asked.

"I never work for someone who's married. My last bwana had no wife until a month ago and as soon as he brought her to the house I left."

"But why?"

"Because the wife watches all the time and keeps everything locked away. I can't have some tea when I want it or even some sugar."

"At least you're honest about it," Gabriel laughed, "but if you come to work for me you'll have to do the whole job yourself; cooking, cleaning, washing the car—the lot."

"All right. I'll start today."

A few days later he asked Gabriel to drive his wife to the hospital to have her baby. When he saw her Gabriel realised she was in the early stages of labour, so lost no time in going. The trip was only about three miles but the road was pot-holed and corrugated. He drove as quickly as he dared and was relieved to be able to hand over the patient still containing the baby when he arrived.

That evening he asked Omari for news of his wife.

"She's back, Bwana. She's all right."

"What happened? Didn't she have the baby then?"

"She did. It's a boy."

"Who drove her home?"

"No one. She walked."

"Do you mean to tell me that since this morning, she's had the baby and walked back here with it?"

"Yes. Why not? I'll call her."

He returned in a few minutes followed by his wife carrying the baby in her arms. He was wrapped in a coloured cotton cloth, and when Gabriel pulled this aside he saw a little reddish-brown face with tightly closed eyes."

"What are you calling him?" he asked.

"Sadiki."

"Sadiki," he repeated after her, touching the infant's forehead. "*Jambo*, Little Bwana," he whispered, "welcome to this Valley of Tears."

***

The next two years saw Gabriel and the team in several locations. On the way back to Mwanza to plan for the next, Rashidi told Gabriel he was not well. "I am having pain in my side, and I wakes up all wet in the night."

"Do you think it's malaria?"

"No. I am not having illness like this before."

"How long has it been going on?"

"About six or eight weeks."

Gabriel examined him and found he had abnormal chest sounds. "I'll take you for a chest X-ray tomorrow," he told him.

The X-ray films showed Rashidi had extensive tuberculosis in one lung with evidence of spread to the other. He was admitted to hospital for preliminary treatment but, as any hope of a cure would require prolonged hospital care, it was decided that he would be better off in hospital in Mombasa close to his family. Gabriel drove him to the dockside to board the lake steamer for Kisumu in Kenya whence he could take the train home. They shook hands in farewell, "Take care of yourself. Do what the doctors tell you, and write to let me know how you are getting on."

"Yes Doctor, I will."

"Some day I'll come to see you. So it is important that you write to tell me how you are and I'll know whether to come laughing or looking sad."

"Come laughing, even if you're feeling sad."

"All right, I will. Goodbye now. God bless you."

"*Kwa heri.*"

* * *

Gabriel's next project took him to villages in the Rufiji District in eastern Tanganyika. The people there were suffering the effects of flooding and food was in very short supply. None of the team had ever worked in an area where the effects of famine were more in evidence. The villages were silent because the children were not playing.

Such conditions produce in the visitor a feeling of compassion but for Gabriel was the added realisation of his own uselessness. He had no need to be there as an investigator; he should have food and medicines and, with the aid of the appropriate experts, be engaged in flood control or, if this were impossible, be alleviating hunger and disease.

European states had made themselves responsible for this part of Africa for nearly a century but the benefits to the native people were hard to find.

Gabriel was sitting at a table going through the records of the day's work by the light of a paraffin lamp when he heard a car outside. He went to the opening of the tent and was greeted with a raucous, "*Jambo*, Angel, me wild Irish boy."

"Sandy," cried Gabriel, "what the hell are you doing here?"

"Elephants, dear boy. I'm after elephants."

"But I didn't know you came here. I thought you worked only in the Serengeti area."

"Oh no. I go where I'm needed."

"Come on in, and tell me all about it."

As Gabriel poured out the beer, Sandy explained his presence. "I heard you lot were in the district. My camp is about ten miles away and I thought I'd nip over to see you. I've been shooting elephants that have been doing a great deal of damage to what few crops there are around here. The locals have been asking for help. Of course, the meat from the animals is a godsend to them under the circumstances."

"It's a shame to have to kill them."

"You wouldn't say that if you saw your year's work being destroyed and, anyway, not only is there some meat for everyone but the proceeds from the sale of the ivory helps as well."

"You're right of course but I'm sure that with proper management there'd be room for both people and elephants. Christ knows the bloody country is big enough."

"It is but any money there is has to be spent on people. You should know that, Angel. What are you doing here anyway? Any bloody fool knows what's wrong with this lot; they just need a few square meals. I'm more use to them than you are. Have you ever thought of that?"

Gabriel did not answer. He opened another bottle and gave it to Sandy.

"Well aren't I?" persisted Sandy. "If you want to give these people a hand, come and shoot an elephant with me tomorrow. At least they can eat that, which is more than can be said for all this bumph you have here. I can lend you a gun."

"Could I? Could I go with you?"

"Of course. I'll show you what to do."

"You're on," said Gabriel, delighted, despite his concern for the elephants. "What time do we start?"

"Be at my camp first thing in the morning, just before sunrise. It's easy to find. Have you ever shot anything?"

"Only rabbits."

"Well at least you'll know how to fire a gun but there's a big difference between what you've used and an elephant gun. It has a kick like a mad mule."

"I'll manage all right but you must give me some idea where I should aim and let me have a few practice shots at a target to let me get the feel of the thing before we go."

"There's nothing to it," said Sandy and went on to explain how to aim for brain and heart shots, making little diagrams on a piece of paper.

They spent the rest of the evening chatting about the famine, the state of the roads, and the whereabouts and activities of acquaintances.

"Where's Wilson, by the way?" Sandy enquired. "I haven't seen him around the camp."

"I don't know. He went to Uganda when I went on leave and didn't come back. I don't know what's happened him. Why do you ask?"

"I just wondered. You know he once worked for me? Did he ever make you rissoles and hamburgers."

"Yes he did, and bloody good they were too."

"You wouldn't say that if you saw him making them. When I did it turned me over."

"Why, whatever did he do?"

"It wasn't that they weren't good, they were delicious. It was the way he made them."

"How? Tell me."

"Well, when you get your mixture ready: meat, flour, eggs, spices, all that stuff, you take lumps and fashion them into spheres of suitable size for cooking."

"Yes, I know."

"I happened on him one day when he was in the middle of this but instead of rolling the stuff on the table, he picked up two lumps and, using the palms of his hands, rolled them around on his bare chest, like this." And he made rotatory movements in imitation of Wilson.

'Oh no!" exclaimed Gabriel, holding his hand to his mouth in disgust.

"But there's more." Sandy continued, "he went on to make hamburgers by flattening rissoles in his armpits."

"Stop, stop," pleaded Gabriel. "I've eaten hundreds of them. I'll never touch another, no matter who makes them?"

It was at this point that Sandy stood up to go, giving Gabriel directions to his camp.

Gabriel was there before sunrise eating some of Sandy's stew. At target practice Sandy told him, "Hold the gun tightly up to your shoulder, making sure the safety catch is off, that it's in the firing position. This is very important. You'll have only time for one shot when the balloon goes up, and if you have to fumble with the safety catch, the animal could be on top of you before you're ready. Don't be deceived by an elephant's bulk, they can move much faster than you can."

Gabriel held the gun and followed Sandy's instructions. He took aim at an empty can, fired and missed. The recoil was stronger than he had expected, nearly knocking him over.

"Not bad," said Sandy. "You were about a foot to the left and a bit too low. Try again."

Gabriel fired several more shots before Sandy considered him proficient. "If the elephant stands sideways to you, at about five yards, kneeling down, you'll get it, sure as shit," he declared.

He led the way to the jeep and drove for about four miles to reach the Rufiji River. "We'll leave the car here," he said, "and go on on foot."

The land was flat and covered in tall elephant grass which stretched from the track leading from the river to an area of raised ground covered with trees about a mile to the south. Sandy believed the elephants to be somewhere in the grassy plain on the move towards the trees to be in the shade during the heat of the day.

"Once we get in that grass we won't be able to see a bloody thing until we reach the trees," Sandy said, "so stick close to me, but if we get separated follow the trail back to the car, then you won't get lost."

Getting lost was a real possibility, and Gabriel was beginning to feel some trepidation at the prospect of going into the grass at all. He also considered what might happen if the elephants had a change of plan and decided to return to the river. They, too, would follow the same trail.

"What'll we do if they come back this way?"

"Don't worry. Once they've had their morning drink and a bathe they won't come back until the evening, and anyway when they do, there'll be fewer of them."

"Why's that?"

"We'll have bagged a couple by then, that's why. Really Angel, where's your hunting instinct?"

"There's nothing wrong with my hunting instinct. It's my self-preserving instinct that comes first with me. We won't have a chance in this long grass if one of the fuckers wants to have a go at us. I've heard that elephants are the most dangerous animals in Africa."

"We'll be all right. Just hold on to the gun and fire; the noise alone will frighten off the bastards."

"I hope you're right," Gabriel said, shouldering the gun.

"Sure we will. Come on, get the lead out. Tally ho!"

Sandy plunged into the grass closely followed by Gabriel. They walked for some time without speaking. Gabriel found the going very heavy. The ground was hard and potted with holes made by the elephants' feet when it had been muddy. As well as these obstacles there were mounds of dung of differing vintages to be negotiated. After fifteen minutes Gabriel signalled a halt.

"What is it?" Sandy asked.

"Let's rest for a while."

"No, we must go on. We're not near them yet."

"Well I hope this'll be worthwhile," grumbled Gabriel.

They set off again and did not stop until they reached a mound of earth about six feet higher than its surroundings. Sandy climbed on to it and looked all around. "The trees are only about five hundred yards away," he announced. "I saw some being shaken, so our friends are still about. Keep your eyes peeled, and whatever you do, don't shoot me for Christ's sake."

He returned to Gabriel's side and they went ahead again. Gabriel felt his heart sink. He had been secretly hoping that the elephants had penetrated deeply into the wood where they would be unable to follow but nevertheless he fell in behind Sandy, checking the gun to make sure it was ready to fire. They continued on until Sandy put a finger to his lips for silence and stopped. Gabriel could hear the noise of trees being shaken and branches broken, as well as a low irregularly intermittent rumbling sound.

"What's that?" he whispered in Sandy's ear.

"What's what?"

"That sound, the rumbling?"

"Farts."

"What?"

"Farts, you fool. They're elephant farts. They do it all the time. It's all that grass and rotting fruit they eat which ferments inside them and makes gas. If they didn't fart all the time, they'd explode. Now shut up and come on."

Gabriel, despite his fears, was tempted to laugh, but the thought of a herd of wild elephants, however flatulent, within a few yards of him made his mouth dry with apprehension and, as Sandy moved on again, he followed with the gun at the ready, close to his shoulder.

After a short distance, Sandy aimed his gun and, as he cleared the tall grass, fired. Gabriel could not see what he was firing at though he was standing just behind him.

"Fire!' screamed Sandy.

"Where?"

"There, right in front of us."

"Where, where?"

As he shouted, Gabriel saw just ahead of him, what appeared to be a greyish-red wall moving. It was a full-grown elephant. He had been unable to see it until it moved. He looked along the shaking barrel of the gun to the elephant's head which was facing him with upraised trunk and flapping ears. Sandy fired again and a puff of dust flew from the top of the elephant's head as the bullet ricocheted off the hard skin.

Gabriel stood, his brain in neutral. The elephant remained immobile, swaying back and forth, and then turned away to follow the rest of the herd which had trampled off deeper into the trees on hearing the first shot.

"Why the hell didn't you shoot?" demanded Sandy.

"I couldn't see the bloody thing till it moved. It's incredible what camouflage can do; an animal as big as that, all but invisible in this cover."

"That's why they're here; it's where they belong."

Gabriel sat down to rest, and to compose himself. "What'll we do now?" he asked.

"We might as well go back. There's no chance of another shot at any of that herd today."

"Thank God for that. I've never been so bloody scared in my life. You know, that animal only had to take a step forward and I was dead. I'm still shaking."

"They very rarely charge. That one was probably more frightened than you were. Maybe it's just as well you didn't fire; you might have annoyed him, and I'd be picking up pieces of squashed doctor now."

They sat quietly for some time before Sandy said, "Come on. Let's go back. At least you've got something to tell your grandchildren."

"An experience I could have done without," remarked Gabriel.

"Nonsense, Angel. You must admit it was bloody exciting. Tourists pay a hundred pounds a day for what we've had for nothing."

They returned to the jeep and drove to Sandy's camp. "I'll have another go at that lot tomorrow," he said as Gabriel was about to leave him, "but I'll take someone with me who can see an elephant when he walks into it."

***

By the time they were finished in the Rufiji District, Gabriel was due to return to Europe again. He had had several letters from Rashidi, and travelled via Mombasa to see him.

When he stepped on the tarmac at Port Reitz airport, Rashidi was there. He looked very well and was wreathed in smiles as Gabriel walked towards him. He was carrying a longbow and some arrows in one hand and a coloured cloth bundle in the other. He put everything on the ground before he could shake hands, which he did while holding his right wrist as usual. "*Jambo*, Doctor," he said, "I am very happy to greets you."

"*Jambo*, Rashidi. You're looking very well. How are you?"

"Much better. All the pain is gone but I'm crying for you."

By this he meant he had missed Gabriel, who said, "Well, I miss you too. I have nobody now for conversation in the evenings. You would have liked being in Rufiji with us and seeing the big river. You could have come on an elephant hunt with me."

"I would not go to hunts elephants, but the river sounds nice. The people there are very native, though."

"What do you mean, very native?"

"They has no clothes, like the Masai."

"Whoever told you that is wrong. They do wear clothes but they are very poor and have very little of anything. Nothing can grow on the flooded land, and even the baboons we saw in the bush were undersized and skinny. Never mind all that, how are your wife and children?"

"My wife is staying with me again. She is well, and so are the children. There is a new baby coming and if it's a boy we are calling him after you."

"That's very flattering but I think you should give him a Muslim name, otherwise the angel at the gate of heaven might think he's a Christian and put him in the wrong place, or even send him away."

"We can give him two names but remember that the Angel Gabriel is in the Koran, so it will be all right to call him Khamis Gabriel bin Rashidi. He will have my father's name and yours."

"That'll be fine; with names like that he'd get in anywhere."

"But you must get your own wife, Doctor, and the children."

"You think I should get married?"

"Oh yes. It is good for a man to be married."

"I've yet to meet anyone I wanted to marry but when I do, I will."

They chatted until the aircraft was ready to go. Gabriel said, "It's time for me to get on board again now."

Rashidi picked up the bundle and handed it over, "These is eggs for you, in case you gets hungry."

"Thank you very much but there will be food in the aeroplane and I think you had better keep these for the children."

Rashidi took back the eggs and put them on the ground again. Then he picked up the bow and arrows. "These is made for you by the Digo, a present."

"Thank you. They are beautifully made, I would love to have them."

"You must go, Doctor."

"Yes. Goodbye."

They shook hands, Gabriel asking, "Can't you even say goodbye without holding your wrist? Don't you trust me yet?"

"Yes, but it's the custom."

"So be it. Goodbye then, and God bless you. Take care of yourself."

"Goodbye. The God is loving you."

Gabriel walked to the aircraft, climbed the steps, manoeuvred the bow and arrows through the doorway, turned to wave, and went in to take his seat.

He was in London the next day. The Rufiji, Mombasa, the mountains and plains, the lakes of his world and the people who lived in it were gone, and he wondered what he was doing in such a noisy, crowded place.

Chapter 9

Gabriel was to stay away for over a year, taking his leave and studying as a postgraduate student in a London hospital. He was feeling sorry for himself having to endure an English winter when he saw a girl in the hospital canteen who attracted his attention. He did not know how long she had been coming there before he noticed her, but once he did, he hardly saw anyone else. He did not know where in the hospital she worked, but planned to find out. He must get to know her. By following her he discovered she worked in the physiotherapy department, but he could not think of a legitimate excuse for visiting the place long enough to meet her in private. He tried sitting at her table during lunch, but she was always accompanied by some of her colleagues which made a discreet approach impossible. Finally, he decided to follow her out of the dining-room and accost her, but what to say? What to do?

Christmas came and went, and during the holiday Gabriel had been to visit his parents in Dublin. The whole time he was there, the girl was in his thoughts, and he determined that come what may, he would contrive to talk to her. He worried that she might leave her job in his absence, and be lost to him.

She was still there when he returned, but he now had a plan for his meeting. He went to the Royal Albert Hall and bought two tickets for a Sunday night Tchaikovsky concert; women are suckers for Tchaikovsky, he felt sure. He now had a deadline. The concert was to be in two weeks, so he must go into action without delay. It was no use trying to talk to the girl in the canteen; he must catch her on her way to it or from it, and preferably the latter when she was more likely to be alone.

The first week passed without success, but on the Tuesday of the second week, she left alone after lunch. He followed her as she went down the stairs. "Excuse me," he stammered, "do you like music?"

She stopped and turned to him with a puzzled look. She had jet black hair and deep brown eyes; she was adorable. "What did you say?" she asked.

"Do you like music?" repeated Gabriel.

She hesitated before saying she did, but looked at him with her eyebrows raised in puzzlement.

"Oh good! Will you come to a concert with me at the Albert Hall next Sunday night. It's Tchaikovsky—it starts at seven-thirty. If I can get tickets that is?"

Despite his nervousness, he had no intention of telling her that he already had the tickets, for she might think he was being presumptuous, which he was, or that he was only asking her because someone else had let him down.

"Mmmm, all right," she said, more bewildered than enthusiastic.

"Good," he said, trying to appear nonchalant. "I'll go along this evening to see if there are any tickets left. I'll let you know tomorrow if it's on. I must rush now. I have a lot to do before I can leave."

The he walked off smartly before she had time to change her mind. Crafty old thing, he thought of himself.

***

The winter became spring, the summer was one of the best for years and Gabriel's courtship progressed. After the first concert there were more, and he had no doubt that this girl, Shirley, was for him. He began to recognise signs that he was beginning to mean something to her too. She was no stranger to tropical life, having lived in Singapore and Australia, so he was confident that she would readily adapt to life in East Africa. An understanding developed between them; there was no formal proposal.

Gabriel went to Dublin to tell his parents. He was having lunch with them when he said, "I was thinking of getting married."

"Bloody near time," said Mr Gabbett.

"Who is she?" asked Mrs Gabbett.

Gabriel gave an account of events since his visit at Christmas, and told them it was their intention to get married in London, and to visit Ireland before going back to Africa.

The wedding took place in Kensington on a bright but cold October day. There were four guests: Shirley's sister and her husband, one of Gabriel's brothers, and their Aunt Ethel, Mrs Gabbett's sister who lived in Surrey. She had borrowed for the occasion a long-haired fur coat. It was much too big and made her look like a haystack.

The ceremony was short and simple, and when the time came for Gabriel to place the ring on Shirley's finger, across the space between them their eyes were saying. "I love you...I love you."

* * *

On their arrival in Africa Gabriel was to work in a hospital in Dar es Salaam. His days in the bush were over and he and Shirley settled into family life. Their first child was a girl. When Gabriel looked at her lying along his forearm, her head resting on his hand, he had no visions of valleys of tears, only of pride and relief at her safe arrival. Here is the Light of my Life, he thought.

Two years later they had a son. Gabriel wrote to Rashidi to tell him, knowing that he would receive this information with more enthusiasm than he had the news of their daughter's birth. On that occasion, though welcoming the event, he made it clear that he considered daughters inferior: they were nice, but sons were better. When he replied this time he said how pleased he was to know that Gabriel had a son. "Now you is a real man Doctor," he wrote, and went on to tell how he had not been very well, and was going back to hospital for further treatment.

Gabriel did not have another letter for some months, and when he did, he noticed for the first time an air of depression about it: Rashidi was worried about his wife and children and what would happen to them when he was gone. Gabriel sent him money several times before he heard from him again, and it was obvious from the quality of the writing that he had difficulty in holding the pen. He had now left hospital but did not say whether he had been discharged or had left of his own accord.

Gabriel's tour of duty was nearing its end and as the family was returning to Europe by sea he would have the opportunity to visit Rashidi. When they arrived at Mombasa, he hired a car and drove to the village where he lived. He had to leave the car to follow a narrow track to his house. On the way he met a youth, and he asked him its whereabouts. "Rashidi bin Khamisi's house?" the boy repeated.

"Yes."

"Are you *his* doctor?"

"Yes I am. Where is he? Which is his house?"

"He is dead."

Gabriel had really known this all the time, but he was shocked to hear it said. "When did he die?"

"A month ago."

"Do you know if his wife and children are here?"

"They are not here. They have gone away."

"Where to? Do you know?"

"No, but I think to her father's."

Gabriel waited a little in silence. Then he started to retrace his way to the car. "Bwana," the boy called after him.

"Yes," turning to face him.

"He was loving you."

***

As the ship entered the Gulf of Suez, Gabriel was leaning on the afterdeck rail gazing into the setting sun and the eternal evening sky beyond it, thinking: I had a youthful dream and it came true. Not many are so fortunate: it is much more than most ever realise.

He started back to help take the children to supper. The past is mine, he thought, the future is theirs with all I have to give.

***

At Suez, Gabriel joined an overland excursion to Cairo while the ship traversed the Canal, Shirley and the children remaining on board .

Like any tourist he inspected the pyramids and visited the museum to see the treasure of Tutankhamen. Then he went to a great mosque. He had never been in such a building. The interior was devoid of furniture; a feature which enhanced its grandeur. He thought of Rashidi and of how happy he would have been to see it; he knew of the Cairo mosques and had told Gabriel that if he ever had enough money he would visit them, after having been to Mecca first of course.

The tour guide invited everyone to feel the coldness of the walls and pillars. Gabriel walked a little way from the rest of the party. He placed his hands against a wall and rested his forehead on the cool alabaster and he had tears in his eyes.

Let his dreams be truth. Let him have his paradise with angels to greet him at the gate. Let the cool waters flow for him along the meadows and by the whispering palms. Let the flowers of the green hills of heaven bloom for him forever, let their perfume scent the gentle breeze and may the birds sing and their music bring him joy.

The Poolbeg
Golden Treasury of
Well Loved Poems

Edited by Sean McMahon

The *Poolbeg Golden Treasury* is a delightful anthology of everyone's favourite poems. There are pieces to be recited aloud, others to be savoured in solitude. The book brims over with patriotic odes, romantic lyrics, stirring ballads, poems evoking a far-off time and place. It ties together the strands of different traditions into a garland of well-loved verse.

POOLBEG

Terrible Beauty

Diana Norman

Constance Markievicz was the most remarkable Irish woman of her generation. Renouncing her Protestant Ascendancy upbringing, she threw herself wholeheartedly into the struggle for independence which dominated Irish politics in the first two decades of this century. A dedicated feminist, she campaigned for equality and suffrage for women, viewing these aspirations as part of the nationalist issue. An ardent socialist, she was committed, alongside Connolly and Larkin, to the cause of Labour and the freedom of workers.

Imprisoned several times by the British authorities and sentenced to death for her part in the Easter Rising of 1916, Constance Markievicz went on to win election in 1918 as the first woman member of parliament, and then the world's first woman Minister of Labour in the first Dáil Éireann. Her courageous action and politial achievements earned her the respect and affection of ordinary Irish men and women.

Diana Norman has written a warm and sympathetic biography, in which her subject's personality is shaped by the threefold influences of resurgent nationalism, feminism and socialism. Believing her to have received less than her full due from previous biographers, Diana Norman here restores Constance Markievicz to a pre-eminent position not just in Irish history but in the history of women in the twentieth century.

POOLBEG

In Quiet Places
The Uncollected Stories, Letters and Critical Prose of Michael McLaverty

Edited with an Introduction by Sophia Hillam King

This collection provides a unique and fascinating insight into the mind and artistic development of one of Ireland's finest writers

POOLBEG

THE SECRET ARMY

J. Bowyer Bell

The Secret Army is the definitive work on the IRA. It provides an absorbing account of a movement which has had a profound effect on the shaping of the modern Irish state. J. Bowyer Bell, a specialist in the problems of unconventional war, terrorism, risk analysis and crisis management, has been a research scholar at Harvard and MIT and at the Institute of War and Peace Studies, Columbia University. He is now President of the International Analysis Centre in New York. He has written more than a dozen books, including *Assassin! The Theory and Practice of Political Violence* and *The Gun in Politics: An Analysis of Irish Political Conflict 1916-1986*.

POOLBEG

Destiny of Dreams

by

Michael Bowler

An evocative novel of a 1950s boyhood in Kerry

POOLBEG

A Strange Kind of Loving

by

Sheila Money

A bittersweet memoir of a girlhood in an eccentric
Anglo-Irish family

POOLBEG